PROGRAMMED SUPPLEMENTS FOR

GENERAL CHEMISTRY $\quad$ *VOLUME TWO*

VOLUME TWO

Programmed Supplements

for

General

Chemistry

GORDON M. BARROW

MALCOLM E. KENNEY

JEAN D. LASSILA

ROBERT L. LITLE

WARREN E. THOMPSON

Case Institute of Technology

W. A. BENJAMIN, INC.
NEW YORK   AMSTERDAM

1964

PROGRAMMED SUPPLEMENTS FOR GENERAL CHEMISTRY
VOLUME TWO

Copyright © 1963 by W. A. Benjamin, Inc.

Library of Congress Catalog Card Number 63-19980
Manufactured in the United States of America

*The manuscript was received on May 21, 1963;
this volume was published October 25, 1963;
second printing, with corrections, April 30, 1964*

*The publisher is pleased to acknowledge the
assistance of Paul Orban, who produced the
illustrations; William Prokos, who designed
the cover; and Cyrus Adler, who assisted
with the programming*

W. A. BENJAMIN, INC.

Preface

Any introductory course in general chemistry must have as one of its objectives the effective presentation of a wide variety of topics. An over-all view of chemistry at this level is generally regarded as desirable both for the students who will not proceed further with chemistry and for those who will continue with more detailed and specialized studies of the various areas of science. The general chemistry course must introduce to its students the current theories and unifying concepts of the subject. For the student to achieve a real familiarity with the subject, he must also acquire skill in the solution of the many typical chemical problems; he can then, for example, better appreciate the experimental basis for chemistry because he can do some of the calculations that relate experimental quantities to derived properties and relations.

The lecturer in such a course is, therefore, faced with the problem of dividing his available time between two kinds of topics. On the one hand, he can limit his discussion to rather general principles and run the risk of leaving the average student unable to apply the principles to specific cases. On the other hand, he can include in his lectures the details of problem-solving procedures and risk the loss of interest that often accompanies such material.

In the general chemistry course at Case Institute we are trying to resolve this common problem by using this programmed instructional material to supplement the course lectures and recitations. We have found that such supplementary material allows the student, on his own, to acquire sound techniques for applying to specific problems the general principles developed in lectures or in assigned reading. In this way the student acquires the ability to handle the manipulations and calculations that are such a necessary part of chemistry. Moreover, when this is accomplished with the aid of programmed supplements, the lecturer is freed of detailed drill and repetition and is able to function in his proper role—that of providing the general principles and background, of showing the unifying features of the topics studied, and of generally conveying the exciting story that can be told, at this stage, about the developing field of chemistry.

Our experience, as we have developed and used this programmed material, is that it provides a valuable course supplement that aids both student and lecturer.

Programmed instruction, provided by books or mechanical devices, is already in widespread use in a number of areas and at various levels; its use in chemistry instruction, although of more recent origin, is growing; and there is clear indication that, when properly used, it is an efficient and effective teaching aid. Briefly stated, programmed instruction consists of a logically organized, carefully sequenced series of items (questions). Each item provides information to be learned and also requires the student to answer a question, carry out a calculation, or insert a word or a number. In this way the student is led to the goal of each programmed unit. You will notice, if you are inspecting programmed material for the first time, that individual items taken out of context seems perhaps trivial or pointless or too difficult. To evaluate programmed material you must follow through a sequence of items, as does the student, to see how topics are developed. The ultimate objective of each chapter is stated in the opening discussion. These statements of objectives serve not only to describe the chapter but also to allow students who have already mastered the material of the chapter to recognize this and to proceed with other work.

The topics covered in this book are some of those dealt with in the general chemistry course at Case Institute. The material of the first three chapters, dealing with basic stoichiometric relations, we regard as mainly remedial. The ability to handle this material and to solve problems involving weight relations in chemical reactions in a clear, logical way is essential if satisfactory progress in chemistry is to be made. We therefore assign this material early in our course. The remaining chapters deal with topics that are part of our general chemistry course. Although our students have had a previous chemistry course, most of this material is new to them.

The material in this book and its companion, Volume II, is supplementary. Topics are not treated exhaustively, and some knowledge of the concepts and terminology pertinent to each topic is assumed. For example, in the chapter on equilibrium calculations in Volume II we assume that the student is familiar with the mass-action law and that he can write the equilibrium constant expression for a reaction if he is given its equation. In this chapter, as the title implies, he learns how to make use of such expressions to calculate equilibrium concentrations or quantities. Whenever such specific background information is assumed, we have indicated this in the introduction to the chapter. It is important to recognize that these programmed supplements do not themselves constitute a course and that all the general unifying material necessary for the complete development of the subject must be provided by the lecturer or through reading assignments. Some of this preparatory information is best given before the students are assigned a chapter, and some further discussion of the topic is valuable after the students have developed the familiarity with the topics that comes from working through the chapter.

Proceeding as outlined in the introduction, each chapter will require one to two hours to complete. Thus each chapter provides a convenient assignment unit.

Gordon M. Barrow
Malcolm E. Kenney
Jean D. Lassila
Robert L. Litle
Warren E. Thompson

Cleveland, Ohio
July 1963

Contents

Introduction

When used as a supplement to your work in basic chemistry, this programmed book will increase your understanding of the general principles and concepts essential to further classroom study.

The topics dealt with are those usually encountered in an introductory general chemistry course; but the procedure for using this book—it is a programmed instruction book, not a textbook or problem manual—may be new to you. The material is divided into chapters, and the objectives of each chapter are clearly stated at the beginning. Within each chapter, the material is presented in short numbered items (one or more sentences) that require you to supply a missing word, perform a calculation, or answer a question. Thus, as you are guided through a topic, you are obliged to participate in its development all the way.

For this book to be most valuable, you must write your answer in the blanks provided; only then should you turn over the page to see whether you are on the right track. The instructions are simple: Read and complete the items in numerical order. You will find on the following right-hand page the correct answer, or answers, for each item. The understanding of each item depends upon your understanding of the ideas in the previous items; therefore you should not go ahead unless your answer is the same or equivalent to the answer given. (Your answer need not be precisely the same as long as the meaning is essentially the same.) If your answer is incorrect, do not go on to the next item until you know why it is wrong and have corrected it. Answers to problems may be calculated with a slide rule. The answers given have been rounded off to the correct number of significant figures.

You will find that each chapter builds up to questions which are, in effect, summary problems that will illustrate whether you have mastered the material at hand. The average completion time for each chapter is between one and two hours.

CHAPTER ONE

Thermochemistry

THERMOCHEMISTRY is the study of the heat effects that accompany chemical reaction. These effects have great practical and theoretical significance. Their practical applications are obvious: the burning of coal, oil, and gas for heating purposes; the combustion of gasoline and other petroleum products for transportation; the use of chemical fuels and oxidants for rockets; the sustenance of life itself by the energy released by chemical reactions occurring in plants and animals. The study of these heat effects has led to advances in our understanding of chemical and biochemical reactions, chemical equilibrium, molecular structure, and, in some measure, to all topics of current interest in chemistry.

If you are to read with understanding in the fields where thermochemistry plays a role, you must come to appreciate that, for a given set of conditions, the quantity of heat evolved or absorbed in a chemical reaction is just as definite as is the amount of any product formed. Your understanding of thermal changes will, moreover, be greater if you keep in mind that a chemical reaction is a process in which molecules come together and rearrange and that, during this process, bonds are broken and new ones are formed. In this chapter you will be introduced to some of the methods used in calculating the amount of energy evolved or absorbed in chemical reactions. The way in which these energy changes can be used to obtain the energy required to break chemical bonds and, conversely, the way in which the energies of bonds can be used to estimate heats of reactions will also be developed.

On completion of the chapter you will be able to solve problems like this: From a table of bond energies, estimate the heat evolved or absorbed when 10.0 g of ammonia react according to the equation $2NH_3(g) \rightarrow H_2NNH_2(g) + H_2(g)$. (See page 19 for bond energies.)

1| Temperature is a measurement of the intensity of heat. In most chemical reactions the temperature of the system either increases or decreases. Therefore . . . . is generally evolved or absorbed in a chemical reaction.

18| When 2 moles of gaseous hydrogen iodide (HI) are formed from 1 mole of H_2 (gas) and 1 mole of I_2 (solid), 12.40 kcal of heat are absorbed. Write the thermochemical equation for this reaction:

. . . .

35| Instead of writing the heat as if it were a reactant or product, one can write the chemical equation and then write ΔH for that reaction. For example, the equation $A \rightarrow C + 10$ kcal could also be expressed as $A \rightarrow C$, $\Delta H = -10$ kcal. In the same way, how would the reaction for the formation of H_2O be written?

52| Dissociation energies for diatomic molecules can often be measured and used to calculate the heats of other reactions. Using the data at the right, set up thermochemical equations to calculate the standard heat of formation of $HCl(g)$:

. . . .

. . . .

. . . .

. . . .

17 Heat = (11.6 kcal/g) × (72.1 g/mole) = 836 kcal/mole

$C_5H_{12}(g) + 8O_2(g) \rightarrow 5CO_2(g) + 6H_2O(l) + 836$ kcal

$H_2(g) + \frac{1}{2}O_2(g) \rightarrow$
$\qquad H_2O(l) + 68.317$ kcal

34 exothermic

negative

51
(a) $H_2(g)$	$\rightarrow 2H(g)$	$\Delta H = +104.2$ kcal
(b) $O_2(g)$	$\rightarrow 2O(g)$	$\Delta H = +118.3$ kcal
(c) $H_2(g) + \frac{1}{2}O_2(g) \rightarrow H_2O(g)$		$\Delta H = -\ 57.8$ kcal

$(a) + \frac{1}{2}(b) - (c): H_2O(g) \qquad \rightarrow 2H(g) + O(g) \quad \Delta H = +221.2$ kcal

$H_2(g) \rightarrow 2H(g) \quad \Delta H = 104.2$ kcal
$Cl_2(g) \rightarrow 2Cl(g) \quad \Delta H = 58.0$ kcal
$HCl(g) \rightarrow H(g) + Cl(g)$
$\qquad \Delta H = 103.2$ kcal

2| If heat is evolved in the reaction the temperature will . . . .
On the other hand, if the temperature falls as the reaction pro-

ceeds, one concludes that . . . . is being . . . . by
the reaction.

19| It is often useful to determine the heat absorbed or evolved in a
reaction that can be thought of as the combination of two or more
reactions. Thus when 1 mole of liquid water is formed from $H_2(g)$

and $O_2(g)$, 68.317 kcal of heat are . . . . ; in the further
conversion of 1 mole of liquid water to water vapor, 10.519 kcal

are . . . .

36| On the energy diagram at the right indicate the relative positions
of $[H_2(g) + \frac{1}{2}O_2(g)]$ and $[H_2O(l)]$ and draw an arrow indicating the
combustion process of the previous item.

53| The dissociation energy of ClF can be calculated from the stand-
ard heat of formation of ClF, −13.3 kcal/mole, and the dissociation energies of F_2 (36.6 kcal) and Cl_2 (58.0 kcal). Combine suit-
able thermochemical equations to obtain ΔH for the reaction
$ClF(g) \rightarrow Cl(g) + F(g)$.

1| heat

18| 12.40 kcal + $H_2(g)$ + $I_2(s)$ → 2HI(g)

35| $H_2(g)$ + $\frac{1}{2}O_2(g)$ → $H_2O(l)$

$\Delta H = -68.317$ kcal

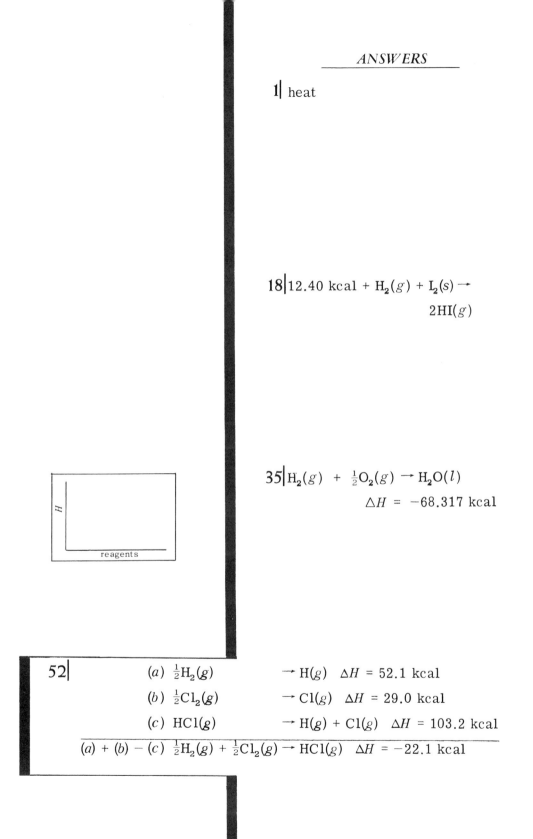

52|

(a) $\frac{1}{2}H_2(g)$	→ H(g)	$\Delta H = 52.1$ kcal
(b) $\frac{1}{2}Cl_2(g)$	→ Cl(g)	$\Delta H = 29.0$ kcal
(c) HCl(g)	→ H(g) + Cl(g)	$\Delta H = 103.2$ kcal

(a) + (b) − (c) $\frac{1}{2}H_2(g)$ + $\frac{1}{2}Cl_2(g)$ → HCl(g) $\Delta H = -22.1$ kcal

3| The word *exothermic* comes from the Greek words *exo*, meaning out of, and *therme*, meaning heat. Therefore the word exothermic is used to describe reactions in which heat is . . . . The temperature of a system would tend to . . . . in exothermic reactions.

20| From the data at the right (from item 19), the total reaction by which 1 mole of $H_2O(g)$ is formed from $H_2(g)$ and $O_2(g)$ can be recognized as occurring with the . . . . of . . . . kcal.

37| The reaction for the conversion of liquid water to vapor (the heat of vaporization of water is 10.519 kcal/mole) can be written

. . . .

54| Using the results of the previous item, draw an energy-level diagram showing the relative energies of $[Cl(g) + F(g)]$, $[ClF(g)]$, and $[\frac{1}{2}Cl_2(g) + \frac{1}{2}F_2(g)]$.

2| increase

heat

absorbed

$$H_2(g) + \tfrac{1}{2}O_2(g) \rightarrow$$
$$H_2O(l) + 68.317 \text{ kcal}$$
$$10.519 \text{ kcal} + H_2O(l) \rightarrow H_2O(g)$$

19| evolved

absorbed

36|

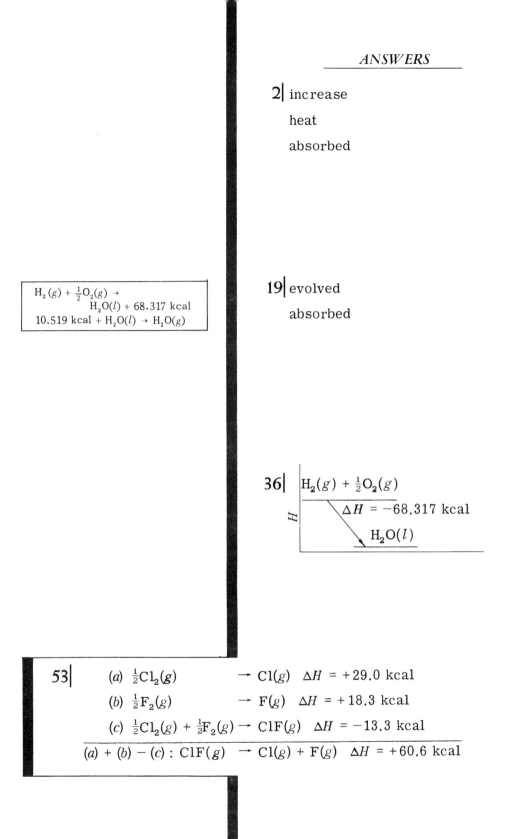

$$H_2(g) + \tfrac{1}{2}O_2(g)$$

H

$\Delta H = -68.317$ kcal

$$H_2O(l)$$

53|

(a) $\tfrac{1}{2}Cl_2(g)$ $\rightarrow$ $Cl(g)$ $\Delta H = +29.0$ kcal

(b) $\tfrac{1}{2}F_2(g)$ $\rightarrow$ $F(g)$ $\Delta H = +18.3$ kcal

(c) $\tfrac{1}{2}Cl_2(g) + \tfrac{1}{2}F_2(g) \rightarrow ClF(g)$ $\Delta H = -13.3$ kcal

(a) + (b) − (c) : $ClF(g)$ $\rightarrow$ $Cl(g) + F(g)$ $\Delta H = +60.6$ kcal

4| The Greek prefix for *into* is *endo*; hence reactions that absorb heat are described as . . .   . reactions. For such reactions the temperature of the reacting system will tend

to . . . .

21| This result is obtained in a convenient, systematic way if the thermochemical equations for the two steps are written underneath each other and are then added as if they were algebraic equations. Carry out this procedure with the data at the right to obtain the thermochemical equation for the reaction $H_2(g) + \frac{1}{2}O_2(g) \rightarrow H_2O(g)$.

38| Draw an energy diagram on the axes at the right to show the relative heat contents of liquid water and water vapor.

55| It is interesting to note that the strength of the ClF bond is (greater, less) than the average strength of the bonds in F_2 and Cl_2.

3 evolved

rise

$$H_2(g) + \tfrac{1}{2}O_2(g) \rightarrow$$
$$H_2O(l) + 68.317 \text{ kcal}$$
$$10.519 \text{ kcal} + H_2O(l) \rightarrow H_2O(g)$$

20 evolution

$$68.317 - 10.519 = 57.798 \text{ kcal}$$

37 $H_2O(l) \rightarrow H_2O(g)$

$$\Delta H = +10.519 \text{ kcal}$$

54

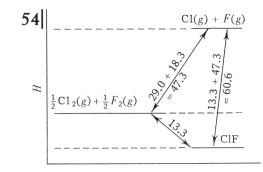

5| Although some reactions proceed with very little heat being evolved or absorbed, most reactions can be recognized either to evolve heat, and therefore be called . . . . reactions, or to absorb heat and therefore be called . . . . reactions.

22| Similarly, one can subtract equations. Thus, the thermochemical equations for the combustion of C(graphite) and CO(g) are

$$C(graphite) + O_2\,(g) \rightarrow CO_2(g) + 94.052 \text{ kcal}$$
$$CO(g) \qquad + \tfrac{1}{2}O_2(g) \rightarrow CO_2(g) + 67.636 \text{ kcal}$$

Subtraction of the second equation from the first (and moving terms with negative signs to the other side) yields:

. . . .

39| As before, equations of two reactions can be added or subtracted to give the equation for a new reaction. When two reactions are added to give a new total reaction, the heat change (ΔH) for this total reaction will be the . . . . of the heat changes for the individual, component reactions.

56| In dissociation reactions the heat content of the products is always greater than that of the reactants. Therefore all dissociation reactions are . . . . reactions, and ΔH for these reactions is always . . . .

4 endothermic

fall

---

21 $H_2(g) + \frac{1}{2}O_2(g) \longrightarrow H_2O(l) + 68.317$ kcal

10.519 kcal $+ H_2O(l) \longrightarrow H_2O(g)$

$H_2(g) + \frac{1}{2}O_2(g) \longrightarrow H_2O(g) + 57.798$ kcal

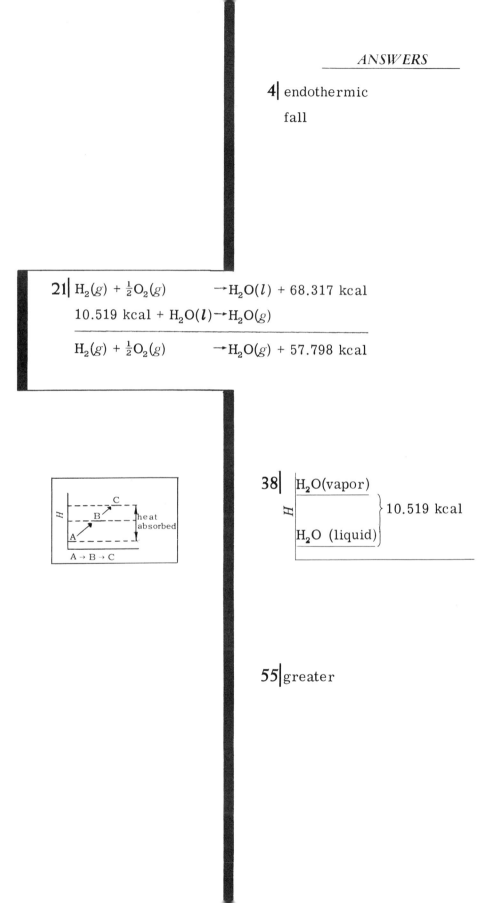

38 H_2O(vapor)

H

H_2O (liquid)

$\left.\right\}$ 10.519 kcal

55 greater

6| Heat can be looked upon as a product of an . . . . reaction. If q is used to represent the amount of heat evolved, it would be written on the . . . . side of the equation for the reaction.

23| In this way, one can deduce the heat effects for hard-to-study reactions from data on experimentally convenient reactions, such as combustion reactions. In the example given, the heat evolved when C (graphite) is burned to $CO(g)$ would be difficult to determine experimentally because, in the reaction, some CO might be further oxidized to . . . . . .

40| Combine the two energy diagrams that answered items 36 and 38 and obtain a diagram that shows the heat of the reaction $H_2(g) + \frac{1}{2}O_2(g) \rightarrow H_2O(g)$

57| From the result of the previous item, one can conclude that the reverse of a dissociation reaction, i.e., one in which a chemical bond is formed, would be a process in which heat is . . . . ; the reaction would be an . . . . reaction.

ANSWERS

5 | exothermic

endothermic

22 | C(graphite) + $\frac{1}{2}O_2(g) \rightarrow$

$CO(g)$ + 26.416 kcal

39 | sum

56 | endothermic

positive

7| The equation, $A + B \rightarrow C$ does not indicate whether the reaction it describes is exothermic or endothermic. Rewrite the equation, using q, so that it represents an exothermic reaction

. . . .

24| The procedure of combining reactions to obtain data on a third reaction depends on the fact that the total heat evolved, or absorbed, in the successive reactions $A \rightarrow B$ and $B \rightarrow C$ is the

same as in the single, direct reaction $A \rightarrow$ . . . . . .

41| Calculate the heat of formation of $H_2O(g)$ from its elements by combining the thermochemical equations of items 35 and 37:

. . . .

. . . .

. . . .

58| The amount of heat liberated in the formation of a bond is called the bond energy and is numerically the same as the heat of

. . . . of the bond.

6| exothermic

   right

23|CO_2

40|
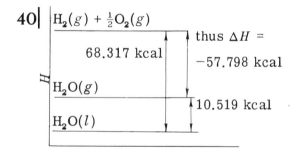

$H_2(g) + \frac{1}{2}O_2(g)$

68.317 kcal

thus $\Delta H =$

-57.798 kcal

$H_2O(g)$

10.519 kcal

$H_2O(l)$

57|evolved

   exothermic

8| Materials appearing on the left side of a chemical equation are called reactants. For an endothermic reaction, therefore, heat can be looked upon as a . . . . For such reactions the amount of heat (symbol . . . . .), would be written on the . . . . side of the equation.

25| Another way of saying the same thing is that the net heat evolved, or absorbed, in the reaction $A \rightarrow C$ is (independent of, dependent on) the number and kind of intermediate steps.

42| The reaction $C(graphite) \rightarrow C(diamond)$ is difficult to perform. For this reaction ΔH can, however, be calculated from the heats of combustion of $C(graphite)$ and $C(diamond)$ of -94.052 and -94.505 kcal/mole, respectively. Calculate ΔH:

. . . .

. . . .

. . . .

59| If a molecule, e.g., H_2O, contains more than one bond, the energy required to break the first bond is not the same as that then re-quired to break the second. However, by determining the total energy required to break all like bonds in the molecule and di-viding by the number of these like bonds, we can obtain an . . . . bond strength.

7 $A + B \rightarrow C + q$

24 C

41
$$H_2(g) + \tfrac{1}{2}O_2(g) \rightarrow H_2O(l) \quad \Delta H = -68.317 \text{ kcal}$$
$$H_2O(l) \qquad\qquad \rightarrow H_2O(g) \quad \Delta H = +10.519 \text{ kcal}$$
$$\overline{H_2(g) + \tfrac{1}{2}O_2(g) \rightarrow H_2O(g) \quad \Delta H = -57.798 \text{ kcal}}$$

58 dissociation

9| A type of reaction in which the heat effects are very important is combustion. Since all such reactions proceed with evolution of heat, they are described as . . . . reactions and heat is a . . . . of the reaction.

26| The heat evolved, or absorbed, in the reaction A → C depends only on the relative energy contents, or *heat contents*, of . . . . . and . . . . . , and not on whether the reaction is stepwise or direct.

43| Complete the energy diagram at the right to represent the relative energies of CO_2, [C(graphite) + O_2], and [C(diamond) + O_2]. The diagram should show that diamond has a . . . . heat content than graphite.

60| For example, in item 51 you calculated ΔH for the complete dissociation of $H_2O(g)$ into atoms: $H_2O(g) \rightarrow 2H(g) + O(g)$, $\Delta H = +221.2$ kcal. This involves breaking two O-H bonds. Therefore, the average O-H bond strength in H_2O is . . . . kcal per mole.

8| reactant

q

left

25| independent of

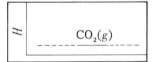

42| C(graphite) + $O_2(g) \rightarrow CO_2(g)$
$\Delta H = -94.052$ kcal

C(diamond) + $O_2(g) \rightarrow CO_2(g)$
$\Delta H = -94.505$ kcal

C(graphite) $\rightarrow$ C(diamond)
$\Delta H = +0.453$ kcal

59| average

10| When 2 moles of hydrogen are burned they react with 1 mole of oxygen to form 2 moles of water. If the water is formed as liquid water, 136,634 cal (i.e., calories) of heat are liberated for every mole of oxygen used up; and the reaction, including the heat, can be written as $2H_2(g) + O_2(g) \rightarrow$ . . . .

27| If the reaction $A \rightarrow C$ is exothermic, the heat content of C must be . . . . than that of A.

44| The *standard heat of formation*, often indicated as ΔH_f, of a compound is defined as the value of ΔH for the reaction in which 1 mole of that compound is formed from its elements in their commonly occurring state at 25°C. Thus, the heat of formation of $HCl(g)$ is . . . . kcal per mole.

61| Estimate the average bond energy of the C-H bond from the data at the right. (Keep in mind that bond energies imply the forming of bonds from gas-phase atoms.)

9| exothermic

product

26| A

C

$$\frac{1}{2}H_2(g) + \frac{1}{2}Cl_2(g) \rightarrow HCl(g)$$
$$\Delta H = -22.1 \text{ kcal}$$

43|

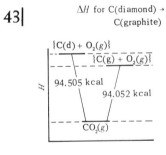

ΔH for C(diamond) → C(graphite)

greater

C(graphite) + 2H$_2$(g) → CH$_4$(g)
$$\Delta H = -18 \text{ kcal}$$
C(graphite) → C(g)
$$\Delta H = +172 \text{ kcal}$$
H$_2$(g) → 2H(g) $\Delta H = +104 \text{ kcal}$

60| 110.6

11| The letters g and l in parentheses in this equation mean that the substances referred to are gaseous and liquid, respectively. Similarly, the symbol s appearing after the formula of a substance would mean that the substance is present in the . . . . state.

28| The thermochemical equation for the formation of $H_2O(g)$ from $H_2(g)$ and $\frac{1}{2}O_2(g)$ shows that the heat content of $H_2O(g)$ is

. . . . than that of $H_2(g) + \frac{1}{2}O_2(g)$ by . . . . kcal.

45| Using the data given in the thermochemical equations at the right, tabulate the heats of formation of the compounds below:

Compound	ΔH_f, kcal
$H_2O(l)$	. . . .
$H_2O(g)$	. . . .
$NH_3(g)$	. . . .

62| A table of such general, approximate bond energies is given on page 19. We can use such a table of bond energies to estimate heats of formation. For instance, we may combine the thermochemical equations for the dissociation of H_2, $N_2(N\equiv N)$, and N-H bonds to estimate the heat of formation of NH_3. Combine suitable equations to do this:

. . . .

. . . .

. . . .

$\frac{3}{2}H_2(g) + \frac{1}{2}N_2(g) \rightarrow NH_3(g)$ ΔH = ...

$10\,|\;2H_2O(l) + 136{,}634$ cal

$$H_2(g) + \tfrac{1}{2}O_2(g) \rightarrow$$
$$H_2O(g) + 57.798 \text{ kcal}$$

$27\,|\,$less

$$H_2(g) + \tfrac{1}{2}O_2(g) \rightarrow H_2O(l)$$
$$\Delta H = -68.32 \text{ kcal}$$
$$2H_2(g) + O_2(g) \rightarrow 2H_2O(g)$$
$$\Delta H = -115.60 \text{ kcal}$$
$$N_2(g) + 3H_2(g) \rightarrow 2NH_3(g)$$
$$\Delta H = -22.08 \text{ kcal}$$

$44\,|\,-22.1$

$61\,|$

(a) $C(\text{graphite}) + 2H_2(g) \rightarrow CH_4(g) \quad \Delta H = -18$ kcal

(b) $C(\text{graphite}) \qquad\qquad \rightarrow C(g) \quad \Delta H = +172$ kcal

(c) $\qquad\qquad\qquad H_2(g) \rightarrow 2H(g) \quad \Delta H = +104$ kcal

(a) $-$ (b) $-$ 2(c) $C(gr) + 4H(g) \rightarrow CH_4(g) \quad \Delta H = -398$ kcal
and C–H bond energy $= \tfrac{1}{4}(398) = 99$ kcal

12| The equation at the right (from item 10) is an example of a thermochemical equation. It differs from ordinary equations in that it not only includes . . . . in the equation but also indicates the . . . . of the chemical reagents.

29| We write ΔH for the difference in the heat content of the products and reactants of a reaction: $\Delta H = H(\text{products}) - H(\text{reactants})$. (The Greek letter Δ is commonly used to indicate increments or differences.) ΔH for the reaction of the previous item is

. . . . kcal. (Be careful with the sign of your answer.)

46| The standard heat of formation of a compound, which is given the symbol . . . . , is defined as the value of ΔH for the reaction in which . . . . is formed from . . . .

. . . .

63| Similarly, set up thermochemical equations to estimate the heat of formation of OF_2:

. . . .

. . . .

. . . .

. . . .

$2H_2(g) + O_2(g) \rightarrow$
$\quad 2H_2O(l) + 136{,}634 \text{ cal}$

11| solid

$H_2(g) + \frac{1}{2}O_2(g) \rightarrow$
$\quad H_2O(g) + 57.798 \text{ kcal}$

28| less

57.798

illus. – question 63

O—F
|
F

45|

Compound	ΔH_f, kcal
$H_2O(l)$	-68.32
$H_2O(g)$	-57.80
$NH_3(g)$	-11.04

62|

(a) $\frac{3}{2}H_2(g)$ $\rightarrow 3H(g)$ $\quad \Delta H = \frac{3}{2}(104.2) \text{ kcal}$

(b) $\frac{1}{2}N_2(g)$ $\rightarrow N(g)$ $\quad \Delta H = \frac{1}{2}(226) \text{ kcal}$

(c) $3H(g) + N(g)$ $\rightarrow NH_3(g)$ $\quad \Delta H = 3(-93) \text{ kcal}$

_____

$(a) + (b) + (c)$ $\frac{3}{2}H_2(g) + \frac{1}{2}N_2(g) \rightarrow NH_3(g)$ $\quad \Delta H = -10 \text{ kcal}$

13| If the equation at the right were written to show the formation of

1 instead of 2 moles of water (in which case only . . . . . as much heat would be evolved) the thermochemical equation would be

. . . .

30| The definition of the change in heat content as ΔH =

. . . . is consistent with the usual way of treating changes. Thus the change in weight of a person during a year would be determined by taking his weight at the end of the year

and subtracting his weight at the . . . . of the year.

47| Another type of reaction of interest in connection with the strength of chemical bonds is that in which bonds are broken to form atoms. The heat required to dissociate 1 mole of gaseous Cl_2 molecules, for example, is 58.0 kcal, and the thermochemical equation, using ΔH to indicate the heat for this reaction, is

. . . .

64| Heats of reactions involving only diatomic molecules can be calculated quite accurately from bond energies, since these are directly determined and are not *average* bond energies. Set up the thermochemical equations to calculate the heat of the reaction $ClF(g) + HCl(g) \rightarrow Cl_2(g) + HF(g)$.

$2H_2(g) + O_2(g) \rightarrow 2H_2O(l) + 136{,}634$ cal

ANSWERS

12 heat

physical state

29 −57.798

46 ΔH_f

1 mole of the compound

its elements in their commonly occurring state.

63

$$F_2(g) \rightarrow 2F(g) \quad \Delta H = 36.6 \text{ kcal}$$

$$\tfrac{1}{2}O_2(g) \rightarrow O(g) \quad \Delta H = 59.2 \text{ kcal}$$

$$2F(g) + O(g) \rightarrow OF_2(g) \quad \Delta H = 2(-44) \text{ kcal}$$

$$F_2(g) + \tfrac{1}{2}O_2(g) \rightarrow OF_2(g) \quad \Delta H = +8 \text{ kcal}$$

14| The equation that answers the previous item illustrates the third
difference that is sometimes observed when the heat effects ac-
companying a reaction are shown, namely, that the coefficients
are sometimes . . . .

31| In exothermic reactions heat is evolved, and a diagram like that
at the right can be drawn. The heat content (H) of the products is
. . . . than that of the reactants. For such reactions the value
of ΔH will be   (positive, zero, negative)

48| The heat (or value of ΔH) of such reactions is a measure of the
strength of the . . . . holding the atoms together in the molecule.

65| Heats of reactions involving polyatomic molecules can be esti-
mated from the table of bond energies, but the values obtained
are approximate because the energy of a bond is not exactly the
same in all molecules. Set up the thermochemical equations to
estimate the heat of the reaction $NH_3(g) + 3Cl_2(g) \rightarrow NCl_3(g) + 3HCl(g)$.

13 half

$$H_2(g) + \tfrac{1}{2}O_2(g) \rightarrow H_2O(l) + 68{,}317 \text{ cal}$$

30 $H(\text{products}) - H(\text{reactants})$

beginning

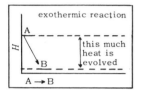

exothermic reaction

47 $Cl_2(g) \rightarrow 2Cl(g) \quad \Delta H = +58.0 \text{ kcal}$

64 $ClF(g) \qquad\qquad \rightarrow Cl(g) + F(g) \quad \Delta H = 60.7 \text{ kcal}$

$HCl(g) \qquad\qquad \rightarrow Cl(g) + H(g) \quad \Delta H = 103.2 \text{ kcal}$

$Cl(g) + Cl(g) \quad \rightarrow Cl_2(g) \quad \Delta H = -58.0 \text{ kcal}$

$H(g) + F(g) \qquad \rightarrow HF(g) \quad \Delta H = -134.6 \text{ kcal}$

$ClF(g) + HCl(g) \rightarrow Cl_2(g) + HF(g) \quad \Delta H = -28.7 \text{ kcal}$

15| Either equation at the right for the combustion of hydrogen shows that the heat of combustion of 1 mole of hydrogen is . . . . cal.

32| Insert horizontal lines with labels *A* and *B* at the right and fill in the blank to complete the energy diagram that would be drawn for an endothermic reaction.

49| If the bond is strong, the heat required for the reaction, known as the *heat of dissociation,* or *dissociation energy,* will be

. . . .

66| The ability to predict approximate heats of reaction is particularly useful when it is necessary to estimate in advance of an experiment how much heat will be liberated or absorbed in a reaction. For instance, in item 62 you calculated the heat of formation of NH_3 as -10 kcal/mole. How much heat would be liberated in the reaction of 3.17 g (i.e., ... mole) of nitrogen in an excess of hydrogen? . . . .

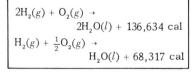

$2H_2(g) + O_2(g) \rightarrow$
$\qquad 2H_2O(l) + 136{,}634$ cal

$H_2(g) + \frac{1}{2}O_2(g) \rightarrow$
$\qquad H_2O(l) + 68{,}317$ cal

14 fractions

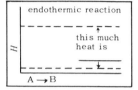

endothermic reaction

H

this much
heat is

A → B

31 less

negative

illus. — question 66

At. wt.	
H	1.01
N	14.0

48 bond

65

$NH_3(g) \qquad\qquad \rightarrow N(g) + 3H(g) \quad \Delta H = 279$ kcal

$3Cl_2(g) \qquad\qquad \rightarrow 6Cl(g) \quad \Delta H = 174.0$ kcal

$3Cl(g) + N(g) \quad \rightarrow NCl_3(g) \quad \Delta H = -144$ kcal

$3H(g) + 3Cl(g) \rightarrow 3HCl(g) \quad \Delta H = -309.6$ kcal

$NH_3(g) + 3Cl_2(g) \rightarrow NCl_3(g) + 3HCl(g) \quad \Delta H = -1$ kcal

16| In previous examples water was formed as a liquid. The heat liberated when 1 mole of water vapor is formed from gaseous oxygen and hydrogen is 57,798 cal. The thermochemical equation showing the formation of 1 mole of water vapor is

. . . .

33| Fill in the following table:

Reaction	Heat (evolved or absorbed)	ΔH (+ or −)	Example
Endothermic			Vaporization of water
Exothermic			

50| The heat of dissociation, or dissociation energy, of HCl is the value of ΔH for the reaction: . . . .

Its value of 103.2 kcal shows that the bond in HCl is . . . . than the bond in Cl_2.

67| From the table of bond energies estimate the heat evolved or absorbed when 10.0 g of ammonia react to form hydrazine (H_2NNH_2), according to the equation

$2NH_3(g) \rightarrow H_2NNH_2(g) + H_2(g)$ (N-N single bond in hydrazine).

$Cl_2(g) \rightarrow 2Cl(g) \quad \Delta H = +58.0 \text{ kcal}$

At. wt.	
H	1.01
N	14.0

15 68,317

32

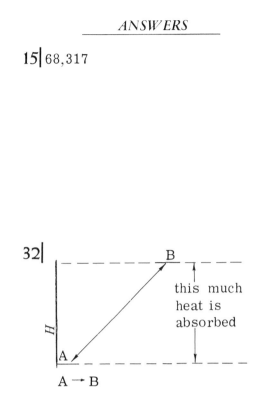

A → B

49 large

66 No. of moles = (3.17g)/(28.0 g/mole) = 0.113 mole

heat evolved per mole N_2
= 2(10) = 20 kcal

heat evolved = (0.113 mole) (20 kcal/mole) = 2.3 kcal

17| The heat of combustion of gaseous pentane (C_5H_{12}) is 11.6 kcal (i.e., kilocalories; 1 kilocalorie = 1000 calories) per gram when the products are gaseous CO_2 and liquid H_2O. The heat liberated in the combustion of 1 *mole* of pentane under these conditions is

. . . . The thermochemical equation for the combustion is . . . .

(*return to page* 2)

34| Since all combustion reactions are . . . . reactions, the values of ΔH for these reactions will be . . . .

(*return to page* 2)

51| The dissociation energies of H_2 and O_2 are 104.2 and 118.3 kcal/mole, respectively. Combine the thermochemical equations for these dissociations with that for the formation of $H_2O(g)$ to obtain ΔH for the reaction $H_2O(g) \rightarrow 2H(g) + O(g)$.

. . . .

. . . .

. . . .

. . . .

(*return to page* 2)

At. wt.
H   1.01
C   12.0

16 $H_2(g) + \frac{1}{2}O_2(g) \rightarrow$

$H_2O(g) + 57,798$ cal

Reaction	Heat	ΔH	Example
33 Endothermic	Absorbed	+	Vaporization of water
Exothermic	Evolved	−	Combustion

$H_2(g) + \frac{1}{2}O_2(g) \rightarrow H_2O(g)$
$\Delta H_f = -57.798$ kcal

50 $HCl(g) \rightarrow H(g) + Cl(g)$

stronger

67 (a) $\qquad NH_3(g) \rightarrow N(g) + 3H(g) \quad \Delta H = +279$ kcal

(b) $\qquad 2H(g) \rightarrow H_2(g) \quad \Delta H = -104$ kcal

(c) $\qquad 2N + 4H \rightarrow H_2NNH_2(g) \quad \Delta H = -410$ kcal

$2(a) + (b) + (c)$ $2NH_3(g) \rightarrow H_2NNH_2(g) + H_2(g) \quad \Delta H = +44$ kcal

or $\qquad NH_3(g) \rightarrow \frac{1}{2}H_2NNH_2(g) + \frac{1}{2}H_2(g) \quad \Delta H = +22$ kcal

moles of $NH_3 = 10.0/17.0 = 0.588$; heat absorbed
$\qquad\qquad = (0.588 \text{ mole})(22 \text{ kcal/mole}) = 13$ kcal

BOND ENERGIES*
kcal/mole

Single bonds

H-H	C-H	N-H	O-H	F-F	Cl-F
104.2	99	93	111	36.6	60.6

H-F	C-C	N-N	O-O	Cl-Cl	Br-Cl
134.6	83	38	33	58.0	52.3

H-Cl	C-Cl	N-Cl	O-F	Br-Br	I-Cl
103.2	78	48	44	46.1	50.3

H-Br	C-Br		S-S	I-I	I-Br
87.5	66		51	36.1	42.5

H-I	C-O		S-H		
71.4	84.0		81		

Multiple bonds

C=C	N=N	O_2
147	100	118.3

C≡C	N≡N
194	226

C=O
170

*Adapted from L. Pauling, "The Nature of the Chemical Bond," Cornell University Press, Ithaca, N.Y., 1960, pp. 84, 85, 189.

A S chemical reactions proceed, heat is evolved or absorbed, and you have learned how to calculate the amount of heat involved just as you earlier learned to calculate the amounts of reactants and products.

For certain reactions special terms are sometimes used, in addition to the useful general term ΔH, the change in heat content. Thus the *heat of dissociation* is the amount of heat absorbed when 1 mole of a compound is dissociated into gas-phase atoms. The *standard heat of formation* is the heat effect associated with the formation of 1 mole of a compound from its elements in their naturally occurring states; the *heat of combustion* is the amount of heat liberated when 1 mole of a compound is completely oxidized by oxygen.

The experimental measurement of heats of reaction, particularly heats of dissociation, allows calculation of bond energies—the amount of energy required to break a bond. For diatomic molecules, bond energies are exactly calculated from heats of dissociation. For polyatomic molecules, only average, approximate bond energies may be calculated, but their values are useful for estimating, in turn, the heats of other reactions.

CHAPTER TWO

Mole Fraction

and

Molality

I N an earlier chapter on solution stoichiometry
(Chap. 3) the value of being able to make calculations that involve the concentration of a substance in solution was demonstrated. It will be recalled that concentration was defined in terms of the number of moles of
solute per liter of solution (i.e., the molarity).

For dealing with what are known as the colligative
properties of solutions, it is necessary to describe
the relative amounts of solute and solvent in different
terms. For example, the freezing point of a solution,
one of the colligative properties, is dependent on the
number of moles of solute relative to the number of
moles of solvent. This ratio, as we will see, is usually
specified by means of either the *mole fraction* or the
molality of the solution.

In this chapter you will learn the definition of these
quantities and how to perform calculations involving
them. Then you will be in a position to study colligative properties of solutions—a subject dealt with in the
following chapter.

1 | The total number of moles present in a solution containing 2.0 moles of alcohol and 3.0 moles of water is . . . . . .

9 | Calculate the mole fractions of the three components in the solution at right. (Note that the sum of the mole fractions is always unity, regardless of the number of components in the solution.)

17 | The number of moles of water in the solution at the right is . . . . . . ; the mole fraction of KCl is . . . .

25 | What weight of ethyl alcohol (C_2H_5OH) would you add to 1000 g of water to prepare a 0.50-m solution? . . . .

33 | A sample of solution containing 0.037 mole of solute in 1000 g of water has the molality . . . . The number of moles of water present is . . . . ; the mole fraction of solute is X_2 = ...

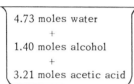

4.73 moles water
+
1.40 moles alcohol
+
3.21 moles acetic acid

0.020 mole KCl
+
1000 g H_2O

At. wt.	
H	1.01
C	12.0
O	16.0

$8\mid 1 - 0.12 = 0.88$

$16\mid n_1$

$\qquad n_2/n_1$

$24\mid$ dissolve the acetic acid in 1000 g of water

$32\mid$ dilute

solvent

2| What fraction of the total moles in the solution at right is alcohol?
. . . .

10| The sum of the mole fractions of all substances in a solution
must equal . . . .

18| The relative amounts of solute and solvent can also be expressed
by the *molality, m*, which is defined as the number of moles of
solute per 1000 g of solvent. In the solution at right m = ...

26| To make a 0.50-*m* solution of ethyl alcohol by adding alcohol to
250 g of water you would not add 23 g, as in the previous item,
but only . . . . × 23 = ... g.

34| What is the mole fraction of solute in a solution containing
0.00241 mole of solute, and 1.96 mole of solvent? . . . .

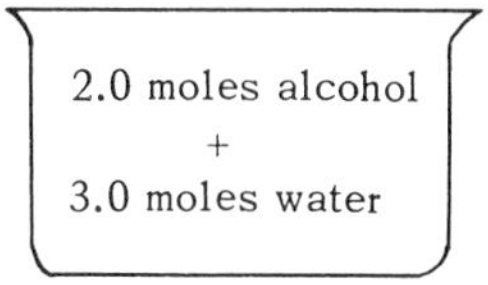
2.0 moles alcohol
+
3.0 moles water

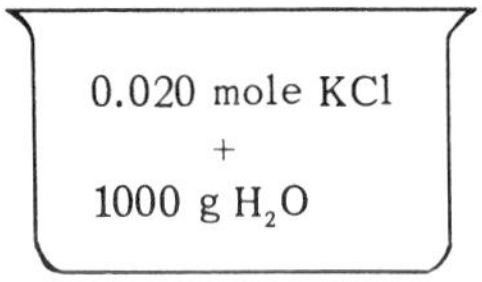
0.020 mole KCl
+
1000 g H_2O

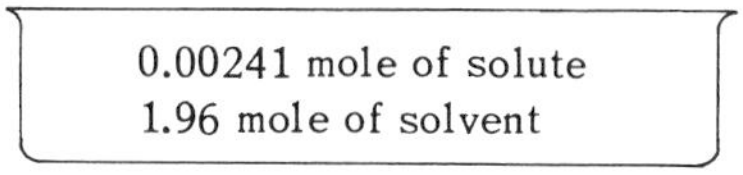
0.00241 mole of solute
1.96 mole of solvent

ANSWERS

1 | 5.0

9 | $X_{\text{water}} = 4.73/9.34 = 0.506$

$X_{\text{alcohol}} = 1.40/9.34 = 0.150$

$X_{\text{acetic acid}} = 3.21/9.34 = 0.344$

17 | $1000/18.0 = 55.6$

$X_2 = 0.020/55.6 = 3.6 \times 10^{-4}$

25 | $0.50(46.1) = 23$ g

33 | $m = 0.037$

$1000/18.0 = 55.6$

$0.037/55.6 = 0.00067$

3| What fraction of the total number of moles (in the solution at

right) is water? . . . .

11| In a solution containing a large amount of substance 1 and a
small amount of substance 2, the first (1) is often called the sol-

vent and the second (2) is called the . . . .

19| In the solution at right the moles of solute per gram of solvent is

. . . . ; the molality, moles per 1000 g, is m = ...

27| To perform calculations involving molality, you must remember,

and make use of, its definition, which is . . . .

. . . .

35| To calculate the molality of the solution in the preceding ques-
tion, we need to know the molecular weight of the solvent (MW_1

= 98). Then: weight of solvent present = ... ; m = moles

solute/1000 g solvent = ...

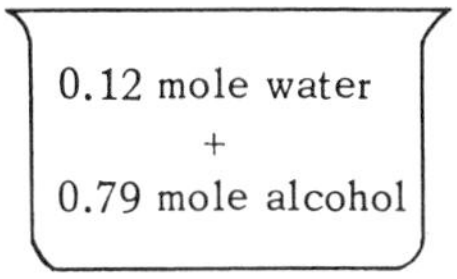
0.12 mole water
+
0.79 mole alcohol

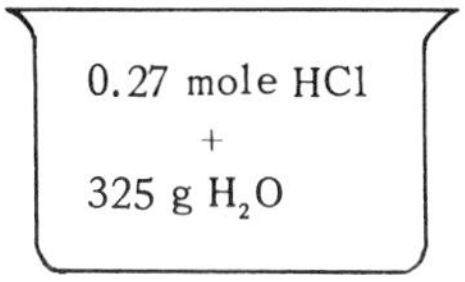
0.27 mole HCl
+
325 g H2O

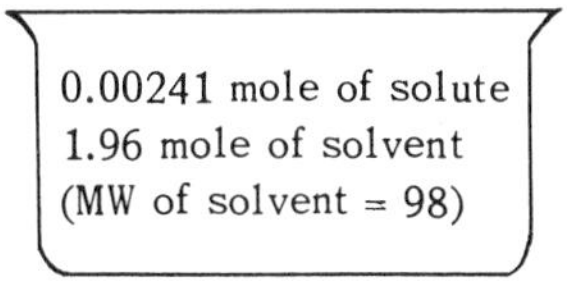
0.00241 mole of solute
1.96 mole of solvent
(MW of solvent = 98)

ANSWERS

2 | $2.0/5.0 = 0.40$

10 | one

18 | 0.020

26 | $(250/1000)\ (23) = 5.8$ g

34 | $X_2 = 0.00241/1.96 = 0.00123$

4 In this solution the fraction of moles contributed by water is 0.12/0.91 = 0.13. We say that the *mole fraction* of water is 0.13.

The mole fraction of alcohol in the same solution is . . . .

12 If n_1 represents the number of moles of solvent, and n_2 the number of moles of solute, then: mole fraction of solvent = X_1

= . . . . ; mole fraction of solute = X_2 = ...

20 A 0.36-*m* KCl solution has . . . . mole(s) of KCl in 1000 g of solvent.

28 To make mole-fraction calculations you must remember that

$$X_{solute} = \frac{\text{moles of solute present}}{\text{total number of moles present}}$$ and that, for very dilute

solutions, this becomes X_{solute} = ...

36 For calculations of both m and X_2, it is necessary to know the number of . . . . . . of solute.

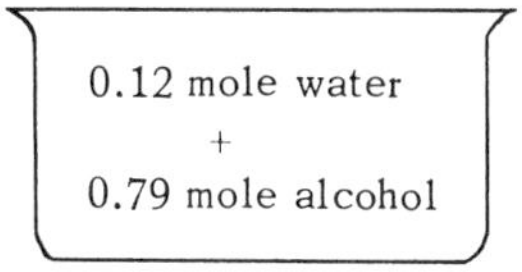

0.12 mole water
+
0.79 mole alcohol

3 | $0.12/0.91 = 0.13$

11 | solute

19 | $0.27/325 = 0.00083$
$m = (1000)(0.00083) = 0.83$

27 | the number of moles of solute
per 1000 g of solvent

35 | $(1.96)(98) = 192$ g
$m = (0.00241/192)(1000)$
$= 0.0126$

5| If n_A moles of substance A and n_B moles of substance B form a solution, the mole fractions X_A and X_B are given by the relations

X_A = ... and X_B = ...

13| The colligative properties of solutions (to be discussed in Chap. 3 of this volume) are usually dealt with in terms of the amount of solute relative to the total amount of solution. Calculations concerning these properties, therefore, involve the variable X_2,

which is the . . . . of . . . .

21| In a solution consisting of 0.062 mole of HCl and 450 g of H_2O the

number of moles of solute per gram of water is . . . . ;

the molality m = ...

29| Calculate the mole fraction and the molality of KBr in a solution made by dissolving 1.0×10^{-3} mole of KBr in 200 g of water.

37| Moreover, for calculations of m we also need to know the weight

of . . . . and, for calculations of X_2, the . . . . of solvent.

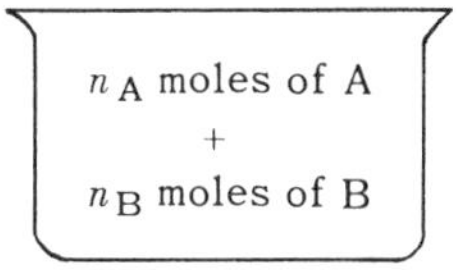

n_A moles of A
+
n_B moles of B

4| $0.79/0.91 = 0.87$

12| $X_1 = \dfrac{n_1}{n_1 + n_2}$

$X_2 = \dfrac{n_2}{n_1 + n_2}$

20| 0.36

28| $\dfrac{\text{moles of solute}}{\text{moles of solvent}}$

36| moles

6 The mole fractions of a solution containing 1.34 moles of A and 0.260 mole of B are: X_A = ... ; and X_B = ...

14 In a solution containing 0.50 mole of water and 0.030 mole of alcohol we would consider . . . . to be the solute; its mole fraction would be X_2 = ...

22 Molality is defined as . . . .
. . . .

30 The number of moles of solute is generally designated by n_2. If we consider solutions that contain 1000 g of solvent, we see that, in view of the definition of molality, the symbol n_2 and the symbol

. . . . . will both stand for the number of moles of . . . .
present.

38 Show again that, for dilute solutions, the values of m and X_2 are proportional to one another (a proportionality that will be used in the next chapter): $X_2 = n_2/n_1 = $ . . . .

0.030 mole alcohol
+
0.50 mole water

ANSWERS

$5|$ $X_A = \dfrac{n_A}{n_A + n_B}$

$X_B = \dfrac{n_B}{n_A + n_B}$

$13|$ mole fraction

solute

$21|$ $0.062/450 = 1.38 \times 10^{-4}$

0.138

$29|$ $X_{KBr} = \dfrac{1.0 \times 10^{-3}}{200/18} = 9.0 \times 10^{-5}$

$m_{KBr} = \left(\dfrac{1.0 \times 10^{-3}}{200}\right)(1000)$

$= 5.0 \times 10^{-3}$

$37|$ solvent

number of moles

7| Note that in the previous item the sum of the mole fractions is 1. Prove that this is true algebraically, using the general expressions for a binary solution.

15| If 0.0010 mole of H_2SO_4 is dissolved in 55 moles of water, the mole fraction of H_2SO_4 is $X_2 = $ . . . .

23| Note the difference between *molality* and the term used in volume stoichiometry, i.e., *molarity*. The latter is defined as . . . .
. . . .
. . . .

31| For dilute solutions $X_2 = n_2/n_1$. We shall now see that X_2 can be simply related to m, the molality. Let MW_1 be the molecular weight of the solvent. For a dilute solution containing 1000 g of solvent, one gets (substituting for n_2 and n_1): $X_2 = n_2/n_1 = $

. . . .

$$X_A = \frac{n_A}{n_A + n_B}$$

$$X_B = \frac{n_B}{n_A + n_B}$$

ANSWERS

6 | $X_A = 1.34/1.60 = 0.837$

$X_B = 0.260/1.60 = 0.163$

14 | alcohol

$X_2 = 0.030/0.53 = 0.057$

22 | the number of moles of solute per 1000 g of solvent

30 | m

solute

38 | $X_2 = n_2/n_1 = m/(1000/\mathrm{MW}_1)$

$= (\mathrm{MW}_1/1000)m$

(*turn to page* 30)

8| In a solution of A and B, if $X_A = 0.12$, then X_B must be

1 − . . . . . $\bar{\equiv}$ . . . . . .

(*return to page* 22)

16| For very dilute solutions, such as that of the previous item, n_2 is

much smaller than . . . . . . In such a case, the expression for

X_2 can be simplified to $X_2 =$ . . . .

(*return to page* 22)

24| What would you do to prepare a 0.15-m aqueous solution of acetic

acid from a 0.15-mole sample of acetic acid? . . . .

. . . .

(*return to page* 22)

32| According to the relation $X_2 = (MW_1/1000)m$, which is valid for

. . . . solutions, the molality of the solution (m) and the
mole fraction of solute (X_2) are proportional to one another; the
proportionality factor depends only on the nature of the

. . . .

(*return to page* 22)

$$X_2 = \frac{n_2}{n_1 + n_2}$$

7| $$X_A + X_B = \frac{n_A}{n_A + n_B} + \frac{n_B}{n_A + n_B}$$

$$= \frac{n_A + n_B}{n_A + n_B} = 1$$

15| $X_2 = 0.0010/55 = 1.8 \times 10^{-5}$

23| the number of moles of solute per liter of solution

31| $X_2 = n_2/n_1 = m/(1000/MW_1)$
$$= (MW_1/1000)m$$

YOU now can calculate molalities and mole fractions of solutions if you are given the number of moles of solute and the weight and number of moles of solvent. Furthermore, you have learned that, for dilute solutions, the molality is proportional to the mole fraction of solute and that these quantities are related by the expression.

$$X_2 = \left(\frac{MW_1}{1000}\right)m$$

In the following chapter, which deals with what are called colligative properties of solutions, you will see that these properties are dependent on the mole fraction of solute and, for dilute solutions, the molality.

CHAPTER THREE

Colligative Properties

of

Solutions

NOW that background material relating the mole fraction of solute to molality has been developed, we can consider four properties of solutions that depend on these quantities. The treatment here is limited, first, to binary solutions, i.e., a single solute dissolved in a solvent, and, second, to those binary solutions in which the solute is relatively nonvolatile and the solute molecules show little tendency to associate, or to dissociate, when dissolved in the solvent.

The principal application of the theory developed in this chapter is the determination of the molecular weight of the solute. After study of this material you will be able to calculate the molecular weight of the solute material from data on the vapor pressure lowering, the boiling point elevation, the freezing point depression, or the osmotic pressure that accompany solution formation. These four properties are known as colligative properties. The types of problems that you will be able to handle after completion of this chapter on colligative properties are illustrated by items 38, 52 to 53, and 77.

We begin by considering the effect that addition of solute to a solvent has on the vapor pressure of the solvent. You will see that the resulting lowering of the vapor pressure of the solvent is one of the colligative properties of the solution.

1| As a solute is added to a solvent, the solvent vapor pressure de-creases, as shown at the right. Because this relationship is linear, with $P = 0$ when $X_1 = 0$, we can write $P \propto$ . . . . or P = (const) . . . .

6| Since the mole fractions X_1 and X_2 are related by $X_1 + X_2 = 1$, then $X_1 =$ . . . . If this relation is substituted in $P = P_0 X_1$ we get $P =$ . . . .

11| For carbon tetrachloride at 20°C, for example, the value of $(MW_1 P_0/1000)$ is 14.0 mm of Hg/1-m soln, and it follows that the vapor pressure lowering when a 1.00-m solution is made using CCl_4 as solvent with any . . . . will be . . . .

16| In the solution at the right there is . . . . g of solute per gram of CCl_4, or . . . . g of solute per 1000 g of CCl_4.

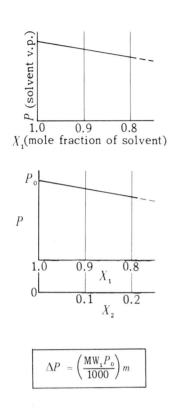

ANSWERS

5 | mole fraction

$$\Delta P = \left(\frac{MW_1 P_0}{1000}\right) m$$

10 | proportional
      solvent

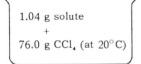

1.04 g solute
      +
76.0 g CCl$_4$ (at 20°C)

$\Delta P_{CCl_4} = (14.0) m$ at 20°C

15 | 1.76/0.041 = 43

20 | molality
      (*turn to page* 37)

2| A pure solvent (containing no dissolved solute) has a value of X_1 equal to . . . . and a vapor pressure denoted by P_0. Application of the equation $P = (\text{const})X_1$ to the pure solvent shows that $(\text{const}) = \ldots \ldots$

7| Addition of solute lowers the vapor pressure of the solvent by the amount $\Delta P = P_0 - P$. Since $P = (P_0 - P_0 X_2)$, we have

$$\Delta P = P_0 - \ldots \ldots \ldots \ldots = \ldots \ldots \ldots$$

12| Similarly, any solution containing a solute in CCl_4 at 20°C that gives a vapor pressure lowering of 14.0 mm of Hg must have

$m = \ldots \ldots$; i.e., it contains . . . . . mole of solute for every 1000 g of CCl_4.

17| For the solution of the previous item, $\Delta P = 2.31$ mm of Hg. Thus there is . . . . mole of solute per 1000 g CCl_4, i.e., 13.7 g solute is . . . . mole.

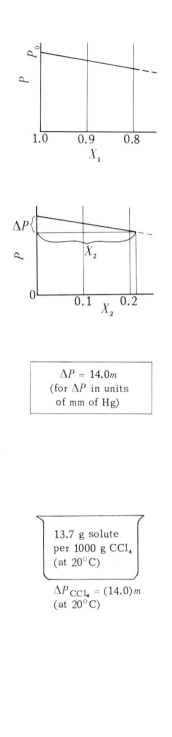

$\Delta P = 14.0m$
(for ΔP in units
of mm of Hg)

13.7 g solute
per 1000 g CCl$_4$
(at 20°C)

$\Delta P_{CCl_4} = (14.0)m$
(at 20°C)

1| X_1

X_1

6| $1 - X_2$

$P = P_0(1 - X_2) = P_0 - P_0 X_2$

11| solute

14.0 mm of Hg

16| $1.04/76.0 = 0.0137$

$0.0137(1000) = 13.7$

3| Solutions whose vapor pressure behavior conforms to the graph at the right (i.e., to the equation . . . .), are said to obey Raoult's law.

8| For dilute solutions obeying . . . . . . law, the lowering of the vapor pressure of the solvent is proportional to the mole fraction of . . . .

13| Since, for a given solvent at a given temperature, $\triangle P$ is propor-tional to . . . . , one can calculate $\triangle P$ from m (or m from $\triangle P$) once the value of the proportionality constant is known.

18| Since 0.165 mole of the solute weighs 13.7 g, the weight per mole (i.e., the . . . . weight) is . . . . g.

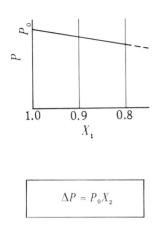

$$\Delta P = P_0 X_2$$

13.7 g (0.165 mole) solute per 1000 g CCl$_4$

2| one (1.0)

P_0

7| $(P_0 - P_0 X_2) = P_0 X_2$

12| 1.00

1.00

17| 2.31/14.0 = 0.165

0.165

4| Raoult's law, which dilute solutions generally obey, states that the vapor pressure of the solvent varies directly as the . . . . of the solvent.

9| The relation at the right was shown in the preceding chapter to be a good approximation for dilute solutions. Thus $\triangle P = P_0 X_2$ can be written $\triangle P = (\ldots \ldots \ldots)m$.

14| When 1.76 g of a solute is dissolved in 1000 g of CCl_4, the lowering of the vapor pressure is found to be 0.58 mm of Hg at 20°C.

The solution must have a molality of . . . . ; therefore, 1.76 g of solute must be equivalent to . . . . mole(s).

19| To obtain the molecular weight of a nonvolatile material you need (1) the . . . . of solute in a known weight of solvent, and (2) the number of . . . . of solute in the same weight of solvent.

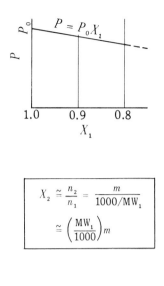

$$X_2 \cong \frac{n_2}{n_1} = \frac{m}{1000/MW_1}$$
$$\cong \left(\frac{MW_1}{1000}\right) m$$

for CCl_4
$\Delta P = (14.0)\, m$
at $20°\,C$

3| $P = (\text{const})\, X_1$ (or $P = P_0 X_1$)

8| Raoult's
   solute

13| m (the molality)

18| molecular
    $13.7/0.165 = 83$

5| For dilute solutions it is more convenient to consider the amount of solute present and to have an expression involving X_2, the

. . . . of solute.

(*return to page* 32)

10| One can see from the expression $\Delta P =(MW_1 P_0 /1000)m$ that ΔP is

. . . . to m and that the proportionality factor depends only on properties of the . . . .

(*return to page* 32)

15| Since 1.76 g of solute in the preceding item is 0.041 mole, there are . . . . g per mole.

(*return to page* 32)

20| The number of moles of solute in 1000 g of solvent (i.e., the

. . . .) can be obtained from the relation $\triangle P = (const)m$ once the value of the constant is known.

(*return to page* 32)

ANSWERS

4 | mole fraction

9 | $\triangle P = (\mathrm{MW}_1 P_0/1000)m$

14 | 0.58/14.0 = 0.041

0.041

19 | weight

moles

THE lowering of the vapor pressure ΔP of a particular solvent at a given temperature has been seen to depend on the molality of the solution and, hence, on the relative numbers of moles of solute and solvent present.

Since this dependence is characteristic of colligative properties, ΔP is a colligative property of the solutions treated here. You have seen how this property can be used to determine the molecular weight of solutes in solution.

Other colligative properties of solutions are often measured more conveniently, and these can be used to determine molecular weights. The relations of these properties to the molality of the solutions can be deduced from the effect of the solute on the vapor pressure of the solvent. The next colligative property to be studied is the raising, or elevation, of the boiling point that accompanies the addition of a nonvolatile solute to a solvent.

21| The vapor pressure of a liquid, as shown at the right, always

. . . . as the temperature rises.

26| Since the vapor pressure curve for the solution lies below and to
the right of the curve for the pure solvent, the boiling point of

the solution is . . . . than that of the pure solvent.

31| Furthermore, in the previous section we saw that $\triangle P$ is propor-
tional to m, the . . . . From this and the preceding discussion (items 29 and 30), it follows that $\triangle T_{BP} \propto$ . . . . . .

36| The K_{BP} values for various solvents at the right can be looked on
as showing the boiling point . . . . for 1-m solutions of
nonvolatile solutes in these solvents.

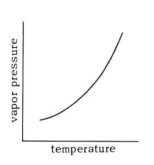

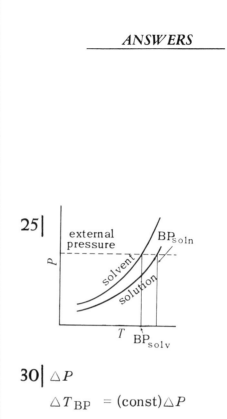

25|

30| $\triangle P$

$\triangle T_{BP} = (\text{const})\triangle P$

$$\Delta P = \left(\frac{MW_1 P_0}{1000}\right) m$$

Solvent	K_{BP}
water	0.51
benzene	2.5
chloroform	3.7
ethyl alcohol	1.2
$\Delta T_{BP} = K_{BP}\, m$	

35| $29/128 = 0.23$

$K_{BP} = \triangle T_{BP}/m = 0.58/0.23$

$= 2.5 \text{ deg}/1\text{-}m \text{ soln.}$

22| The boiling point can be located in the figure as the temperature at which the dashed line, representing the external pressure, and

the solid curve, representing the . . . . of the liquid, intersect.

27| For dilute solutions the vapor pressure lowering will be relatively small. The increase in the boiling point, or boiling point

elevation, will be relatively . . . .

32| With the introduction of the proportionality constant K_{BP} , the

preceding item can be written as the equation . . . .

$=$ . . . .

37| Since K_{BP} for water is 0.51, an aqueous solution that boils

1.37°C higher than pure water must have a molality of . . . .

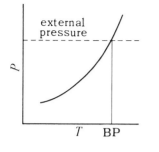

21| increases

26| higher

$$\Delta T_{BP} \propto m$$

31| molality

m

$$\Delta T_{BP} = 0.51m$$
for aqueous solutions

36| elevation

23| As we saw earlier, the addition of a nonvolatile solute to a sol-
vent . . . . the vapor pressure of the solvent.

28| For comparisons of the vapor pressure curves for solvents and
dilute solutions, the curves near the boiling point can be approx-
imated, as shown, by . . . . lines. Label these lines and
the boiling points.

33| As in the case of the proportionality constant between $\triangle P$ and m,
the constant K_{BP} depends on the nature of the . . . . but
is not influenced by the nature of the . . . .

38| A solution of 46.8 g of solute in 1000 g of water has a $\triangle T_{BP}$
value of 0.38°C. The molality of the solution is . . . . In
1000 g of water there are . . . . g or . . . . mole(s) of
solute. The weight per mole, or molecular weight, can thus be
calculated to be . . . .

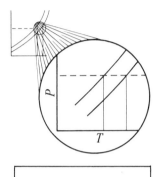

$$\Delta P = (MW_1 P_0 / 1000) m$$

22| vapor pressure

27| small

32| $\triangle T_{BP} = K_{BP}\, m$

37| 1.37/0.51 = 2.7

24| The two vapor pressure curves in the accompanying figure represent pure solvent and dilute solution containing a nonvolatile solute. Label the curves with *solvent* and *solution*.

29| It follows, as the figure suggests, that the boiling point elevation $\triangle T_{BP}$ and the vapor pressure lowering $\triangle P$ are . . . . to one another.

34| The constant K_{BP} can be determined for a solvent by measuring $\triangle T_{BP}$ for a solution of known . . . .

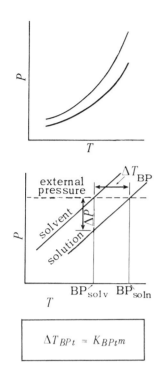

$$\Delta T_{BPt} = K_{BPt}m$$

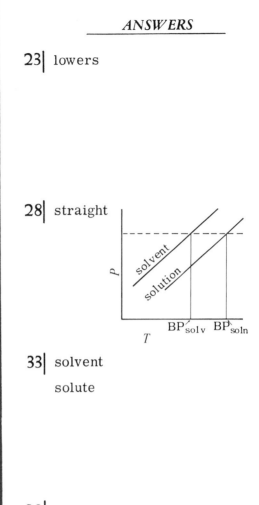

23| lowers

28| straight

33| solvent

solute

38| 0.38/0.51 = 0.75

46.8 g

0.75 mole

46.8/0.75 = 62

(*turn to page* 43)

25| Redraw these two curves, label the axes, and locate on the temperature axis the boiling points of the pure solvent and of the solution.

(return to page 38)

30| Since, for dilute solutions, $\triangle T_{\text{BP}}$ and $\triangle P$ are proportional to one another, we can write the equations $\triangle T_{\text{BP}} \propto \ldots \ldots$ or $\ldots \ldots$ $= \ldots \ldots$

(return to page 38)

35| The molality of the solution at the right is $\ldots \ldots$ The boiling point elevation allows us to calculate K_{BP} for benzene (using the equation $\triangle T_{\text{BP}} = K_{\text{BP}} m$): $K_{\text{BP}} = \ldots \ldots \ldots$

(return to page 38)

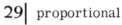

29 g naphthalene $(C_{10}H_8)$

$+$

1000 g benzene (C_6H_6)

boiling point 0.58°C higher
than that of pure benzene

24|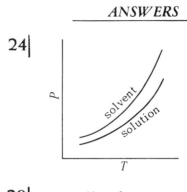

29| proportional

34| molality

YOU have seen that, for a given solvent, the boiling point elevation depends only on the relative number of moles, or molecules, of solute and solvent; therefore, that the boiling point elevation is another colligative property; and that the molecular weight of the solute can be determined from the relation $\Delta T_{\mathrm{BPt}} = K_{\mathrm{BPt}} m$ when the boiling point elevation constant is known.

A third colligative property is the lowering, or depression, of the freezing point that generally accompanies solution formation. Freezing point depressions can usually be measured more easily than vapor pressure lowerings or boiling point elevations and are often used to determine the molecular weight of a newly synthesized or newly isolated material.

39| The freezing point of a pure substance is defined as the temper-
ature at which the . . . . and the . . . . phases are in
equilibrium.

43| The accompanying figure shows that the temperature at which
the solution is in equilibrium with the solid is . . . . than the
temperature at which the solvent is in equilibrium with the solid.

4 | Recalling that $\triangle P$ is proportional to m, the . . . . of the
solution, we write the proportionality equation $\triangle T_{FP} \propto$ . . . . . .

51| The freezing point of pure benzene is 5.5°C and the value of
K_{FPt} for benzene is 5.12. A 0.19-m solution of a nonvolatile
solute in benzene will have $\triangle T_{FP}$ = ... and will start to
freeze at . . . . °C.

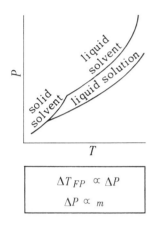

$$\Delta T_{FP} \propto \Delta P$$

$$\Delta P \propto m$$

42|

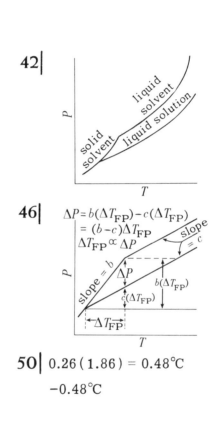

46| $\Delta P = b(\Delta T_{FP}) - c(\Delta T_{FP})$
$= (b-c)\Delta T_{FP}$
$\Delta T_{FP} \propto \Delta P$

50| $0.26(1.86) = 0.48°C$

$-0.48°C$

40| Consider the system at the right containing solid and liquid phases of the same substance. The two phases are in equilibrium if they have the same . . . . pressures.

44| In other words, the freezing point of a solution is . . . . than that of the pure solvent, and we talk about the freezing point . . . . that accompanies solution formation.

48| If the freezing point depression constant K_{FP} is now introduced, an equation similar to that written for $\triangle T_{BP}$ is obtained, i.e.,

$$\triangle T_{FP} = ...$$

52| A solution is made up to contain 3.69 g of an unknown material in 28.8 g of benzene. The weight of solute per gram of benzene is . . . . and the weight per 1000 g of benzene is . . . .

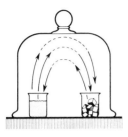

$$\Delta T_{FP} \propto m$$

39 solid
liquid

43 lower

47 molality
m

51 5.12 (0.19) = 0.97°C
5.5 − 0.97 = 4.5°C

41 The vapor pressures of both the solid and liquid depend on the temperature, as indicated at the right. The temperature at which the two curves intersect is the . . . .

45 Label the curves on the expanded portion from previous figures. Locate the freezing points of the solvent and the solution on the temperature axis.

49 The freezing point depression constant for water is 1.86 deg/1-m solution. A 1-m solution will have a freezing point of . . . . °C. A 0.176-m solution will begin to freeze at . . . . °C.

53 The solution in the previous item is found to begin to freeze at 2.8°C. With the information at the right, we see that the molality is . . . . and, since there are 128 g of solute per 1000 g of benzene, that the molecular weight of the solute is . . . .

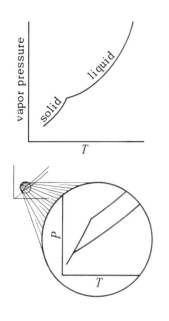

freezing pt. of pure
benzene = 5.5° C

K_{FP} for benzene ≐ 5.12

40| vapor

44| lower

depression (or lowering)

48| $K_{FP}\, m$

52| 3.69/28.8 = 0.128 g

0.128 (1000) = 128 g

42| Generally, when a dilute solution starts to freeze, solid solvent begins to separate from the solution. Label the vapor pressure curves at the right as *solid solvent, liquid solvent,* and *liquid solution.*

(*return to page* 44)

46| The small portions of the vapor pressure curves shown can be approximated by straight lines, with slopes b and c. Show that $\triangle P = (b - c)\triangle T_{FP}$ and, hence, that $\triangle T_{FP}$ is proportional to $\triangle P$.

(*return to page* 44)

50| A 0.26-m solution of sucrose in water, for which $K_{FPt} = 1.86$, will have a value of $\triangle T_{FP}$ of . . . . °C. The solution will begin to freeze at . . . . °C.

(*return to page* 44)

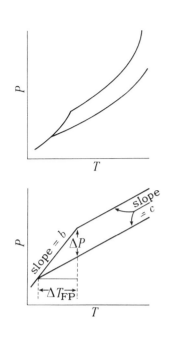

41 freezing point (or melting point)

45

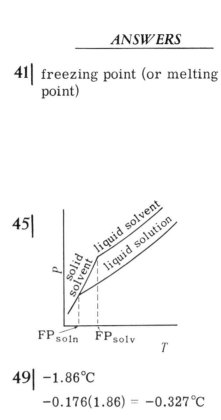

49 $-1.86°C$

$-0.176(1.86) = -0.327°C$

53 $5.5-2.8/5.12 = 2.7/5.12 = 0.53$

$128/0.53 = 240$

(_turn to page_ 48)

THE final property of a solution that depends on the number of solute molecules present, and therefore is a colligative property, is the osmotic pressure that is obtained when the solution is separated from the pure solvent by a semipermeable membrane. (A semipermeable membrane allows the solvent to pass through but prevents the passage of the solute.)

The osmotic pressure can be exhibited by arranging an apparatus as in the first figure on the next page and allowing the system to come to equilibrium. One finds that the solvent flows from the pure solvent compartment into the solution compartment until a certain pressure, shown by the column of liquid, is built up and prevents further flow of solvent. This pressure is called the osmotic pressure. The osmotic pressure can also be illustrated with an apparatus, shown in the second figure, where a pressure can be applied to the solution so that the sensitive flow indicator shows that no solvent is flowing. Again the additional pressure that must be applied to the solution to prevent the pure solvent from flowing into the solution is the osmotic pressure.

You will now see how the osmotic pressure, usually denoted by π, is related to the properties of the solution and how it is used to obtain molecular weights.

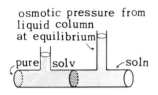

osmotic pressure from
liquid column
at equilibrium

pure solv   soln

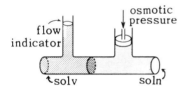

flow
indicator

osmotic
pressure

solv   soln

54| As with the three colligative properties already dealt with, the

. . . . , the . . . . , and the

. . . . , the osmotic pressure π is found, for

dilute solutions, to be proportional to the . . . .
of the solution.

60| The equation $\pi = (const)m$ can be used in the same way as were

the equations $\triangle P = $ . . . . , $\triangle T_{BP} = $ . . . ., and $\triangle T_{FP}$

$= $ . . . .

66| To prevent solvent from flowing through a membrane and into
the solution described in the previous item, one would have to
apply pressure on the solution until the excess pressure is

. . . . atm.

72| The osmotic pressure of a 0.00100-m solution is therefore easily
measurable. On the other hand, the freezing point depression

would be only . . . ., and the boiling point elevation would

be only . . . . and would be measured only with consider-
able difficulty.

78| How much ethylene glycol ($C_2H_6O_2$) must be added to 500 g
of water to lower the freezing point of the water by 5.0°C?

(K_{FP} of water = 1.86.) . . . .

59| $(22.4)m$ atm

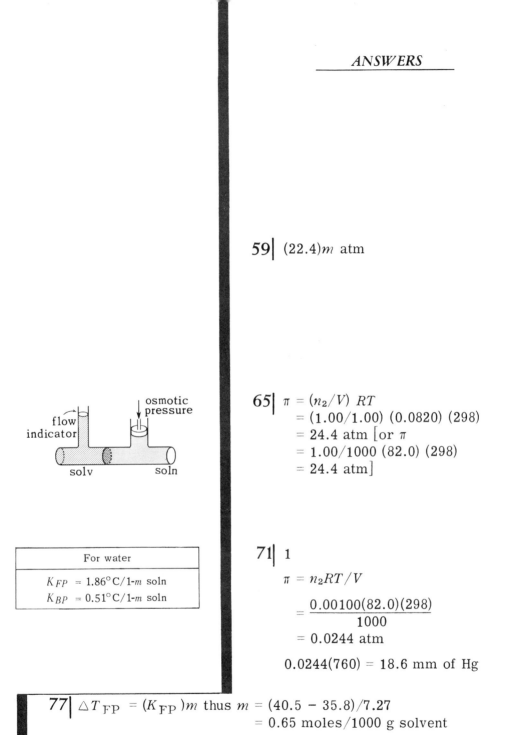

65| $\pi = (n_2/V)\ RT$
$= (1.00/1.00)\ (0.0820)\ (298)$
$= 24.4$ atm $\left[\text{or } \pi\right.$
$= 1.00/1000\ (82.0)\ (298)$
$= 24.4$ atm$\left.\right]$

For water
$K_{FP} = 1.86°C/1\text{-}m$ soln
$K_{BP} = 0.51°C/1\text{-}m$ soln

71| 1

$\pi = n_2 RT / V$

$= \dfrac{0.00100(82.0)(298)}{1000}$

$= 0.0244$ atm

$0.0244(760) = 18.6$ mm of Hg

77| $\triangle T_{FP} = (K_{FP})m$ thus $m = (40.5 - 35.8)/7.27$
$= 0.65$ moles$/1000$ g solvent

wt$/1000$ g solvent $= (0.820/10.00)\ (1000) = 82.0$ g and
mol. wt. $= 82.0/0.65 = 126$ amu

55| The proportionality equation π . . . . can be written between π and m.

61| An interesting looking osmotic pressure equation is found for *very* dilute solutions if we use n_2/V (where n_2 is the moles of solute and V is the volume of solution) rather than the . . . . .

. . . . , which we have been using to express the amount of solute in colligative-property equations.

67| In applying the equation $\pi V = n_2 RT$ one must be careful to have the same units of pressure and volume on both sides of the equation. The pressure units of π and the volume units of V must

therefore be the same as those implied by the value of . . . . . used in the equation.

73| The sensitivity of osmotic pressure is particularly helpful when high molecular weights are determined, since a large weight of solute then corresponds to a relatively small number of . . . . . . of solute.

79| At 27°C, 0.00647 g of a deep-blue hydrocarbon is dissolved in enough cyclohexane (C_6H_{12}) to give 10.0 cc of solution. The osmotic pressure of the solution is 94.3 mm Hg. What is the molecular weight of the blue compound ? . . . .

54| vapor pressure lowering

boiling point elevation

freezing point depression

molality

60| $\triangle P = (\text{const})m$

$\triangle T_{BP} = (K_{BP})m$

$\triangle T_{FP} = (K_{FP})m$

66| 24.4

72| $1.86(0.00100) = 0.00186°C$

$0.51(0.00100) = 0.00051°C$

78| molality needed $= \triangle T_{FP}/K_{FP} = 5.0/1.86 = 2.7$

thus moles of glycol needed $= (500/1000)(2.7) = 1.35$

wt of glycol $= (1.35)(62) = 84$ g

56| If this proportionality were converted to an equality by the intro-
duction of a constant, the value of the constant would depend only

on the properties of the . . . .

62| In very dilute solutions n_2/V is proportional to m. The relation

$\pi \propto m$ can be converted to . . . .

68| A solution of a newly synthesized material produces an osmotic
pressure of 28.3 mm when separated by a membrane from pure

solvent at 25°C. The value of π in atm is . . . . and the

number of moles of solute per 1000 cc of solution must be . . . .

. . . . . .

74| Of the four colligative properties of solutions, ...

. . . . . , ... , ... , and

. . . . , osmotic-pressure measurements are
used most to determine the molecular weights of high molecular
weight materials.

55| ∝ m

61| molality (or m)

R = 82.0 cc atm/deg-mole

67| R

73| moles

79| $\pi V = n_2 R T$

$\pi = 94.3/760 = 0.124$ atm

$n_2 = \dfrac{(0.124)(10.0)}{(82.0)(300)} = 5.05 \times 10^{-5}$ moles in 10.0 cc

weight in 10.0 cc of solution = 6.47×10^{-3} g

and mol. wt. $= \dfrac{6.47 \times 10^{-3}}{5.05 \times 10^{-5}} = 128$ amu

(turn to page 55)

57| One could write $\pi = (\text{const})m$ and determine the value of the constant by measuring π, the . . . . , for a solution of known . . . .

63| Experimental values of π show that, for very dilute solutions, the proportionality constant between π and n_2/V has the value RT for any solvent. We can thus write the equation . . . .

69| The result of the experiment of the previous item would permit the calculation of the molecular weight if, in addition to knowing that there are 0.00152 moles/1000 cc, one knew the . . . . of solute/1000 cc.

75| The four equations that have been used, for dilute solutions, to deduce molalities or molecular weights, are: . . . . , ... , ... , and . . . .

56| solvent

62| $\pi \propto n_2/V$

68| $28.3/760 = 0.0372$ atm

$$n_2 = \frac{\pi V}{RT} = \frac{0.0372(1000)}{82.0(298)}$$

$$= 0.00152 \text{ mole}$$

74| vapor pressure lowering

boiling point elevation

freezing point depression

osmotic pressure

58| With the equation $\pi = (\text{const})m$, and a known value for the constant for the solvent used, one could measure . . . . . and then deter- mine . . . . . for a solution containing a solute of unknown molec- ular weight.

64| The constant R is found to be identical to the gas constant that appears in the ideal gas equation $PV = nRT$. Rearranged to this form, the osmotic pressure relation is . . . .

70| If the weight of solute per liter of solution of the previous items is 8.32 g, the weight per mole, or molecular weight, must be

. . . .

76| Some review items on the material that you have learned in sep- arate sections of this colligative property chapter are now given; Chloroform ($CHCl_3$) has a boiling point of 61.3°C. A solution of 1.68 g of methylcyclohexane (C_7H_{14}) in 30.0 g of $CHCl_3$ has a boiling point of 63.4°C. What is the boiling point elevation con- stant of chloroform? . . . .

π = 28.3 mm n_2 = 0.00152 moles/1000 cc

ANSWERS

57 osmotic pressure
molality

63 $\pi = RT\ n_2/V$

69 weight

75 $\triangle P = (\text{const})m$
$\triangle T_{BP} = (K_{BP})m$
$\triangle T_{FP} = (K_{FP})m$
$\pi V = n_2RT$

59| The osmotic pressure of a 1.00-m aqueous solution at O°C is found to be 22.4 atm. The general osmotic-pressure equation for dilute aqueous solutions at O°C then is π = ...

(return to page 49)

65| Since R has the value 0.0820 liter-atm/deg-mole or 82.0 cc-atm/deg-mole, the osmotic pressure of a solution containing 1.00 mole in 1000 cc of solution at 25°C is calculated to be

. . . .

(return to page 49)

71| A 0.00100-m aqueous solution has about 0.00100 mole in . . . . . liter(s) of solution. The osmotic pressure of this solution at 25°C against pure water would be π = ... atm, or π

= . . . . mm of Hg.

(return to page 49)

77| The freezing point of phenol (C_6H_5OH) is 40.5°, and its freezing point depression constant is 7.27°C/1-m solution. When 0.820 g of a deep-blue hydrocarbon is dissolved in 10.00 g of phenol, the freezing point of the solution is 35.8°. What is the molecular weight of the hydrocarbon?

(return to page 49)

$\pi V = n_2RT$

ANSWERS

58| π

m

64| $\pi V = n_2RT$

70| $8.32/0.00152 = 5470$

76| $\triangle T_{BP} = (K_{BP})m = 63.4 - 61.3 = 2.1°C$

$$m = \left(\frac{1.68/98.1}{30.0}\right)(1000) = 0.571$$

and $K_{BP} = 2.1/0.571 = 3.7$

NOW that you have finished another chapter about solutions, you know that there are four properties of solutions that depend on the number of solute molecules present. The magnitude of each of these four colligative properties is proportional, for dilute solutions, to the molality of the solution and is independent of any other feature of the solute molecules. For this reason, the molecular weight of the solute can be determined from a knowledge of the ratio of the weights of solute to that of the solvent and of the magnitude of the vapor pressure depression, the boiling point elevation, the freezing point depression, or the osmotic pressure of the solution. It is important to remember, however, that the equations in this chapter have been developed for the ideal solution, i.e., a dilute solution of a nonvolatile solute that neither associates nor dissociates in the solvent. You will find, even with these limitations, that these relationships are widely used, particularly for the determination of molecular weights.

A particularly interesting application that you will come to in later studies is to solutes that are acids, bases, or salts and the solvent is water. Then the solute molecules dissociate, and there are more solute particles than the number of molecules of the solute might indicate. Colligative properties are important in the study of such ionizations.

CHAPTER FOUR

Acids

and

Bases

THE behavior of many chemical compounds can best be correlated by classifying them as acids or bases. If the concept of acids and bases is to be used, it is necessary to understand the meaning of these terms.

Since most introductions to the study of acids and bases are concerned with aqueous solutions, such systems will be emphasized here. Moreover, the definition of acids as hydrogen ion donors and bases as hydrogen ion acceptors, a definition due to Brönsted, will be used.

Study of this chapter will provide you with an understanding of the nature and reactions of acids and bases and the stoichiometry of acid-base reactions. You will also acquire the necessary background for the study of acid-base equilibrium calculations in Chapter 6.

1| Positively charged hydrogen ions (H^+) can be produced in the gas phase by removing an . . . . from a hydrogen atom.

10| The Lewis diagram for H_2O is $H:\overset{..}{\underset{..}{O}}:$. The Lewis diagram for
H

the hydronium ion is . . . .

19| Just as H_3O^+ is the conjugate . . . . of the base H_2O, so H_2O is the conjugate . . . . . . of the acid H_3O^+.

28| Of the species H_3O^+, H_2O, OH^- (all very important in acid-base studies), which can act most easily both as an acid and as a base? . . . .

37| HCl is a strong acid, and therefore its conjugate base, ... , is a weak base.

9| water

18| acid

27| HSO$_4^-$

36| accept
weak

2| Since a hydrogen atom consists of a proton and an electron, the species indicated by H^+ in chemical studies is really nothing more than a . . . .

11| Since the oxygen atom of a water molecule has a pair of electrons available for sharing, it can accept a proton. In so doing, it is acting as a . . . .

20| The conjugate base of the acid HCN is . . . . The conjugate base of the acid NH_4^+ is . . . .

29| Using HCl as the acid and NH_3 as the base, write equations for two reactions, one in which H_2O acts as a base and one in which H_2O acts as an acid:

. . . .

. . . .

38| $CH_3 - \overset{\overset{\displaystyle O}{\|}}{C} - OH$ is a relatively weak acid; consequently, its conjugate base, ... , is a relatively strong base.

1| electron

10| $\begin{bmatrix} \text{H} \\ \text{H} : \overset{\cdot\cdot}{\underset{}{\text{O}}} : \\ \text{H} \end{bmatrix}^{+}$ (or $\begin{bmatrix} \text{H} : \overset{\cdot\cdot}{\underset{\cdot\cdot}{\text{O}}} : \text{H} \\ \text{H} \end{bmatrix}^{+}$ etc.)

19| acid
base

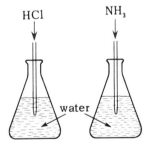

HCl   NH₃

water

28| H_2O

37| Cl⁻

3| Hydrogen ions are very reactive and tend to react so that they share a pair of electrons with another atom. The molecules HCl, H_2, H_2O, for example, have Lewis diagrams (see Chap. 5 of Vol. I)

H : C̈l : , ... , and . . . .

12| Similarly, the hydroxyl ion (OH^-) is a base because it can accept

a . . . . as, for example, in the reaction $H_3O^+ + OH^- \rightarrow$

. . . .

21| The conjugate base of H_2O is . . . . The conjugate acid of

OH^- is . . . .

30| When acid-base reactions involving . . . . transfers occur in aqueous solution, the solvent (. . . . . . .) is not inert; it enters into the reactions.

39| The ion NH_4^+ does not easily give up a proton, i.e., NH_4^+ is a

. . . . acid. This is consistent with the fact that its conjugate base, ... , is a fairly . . . . base.

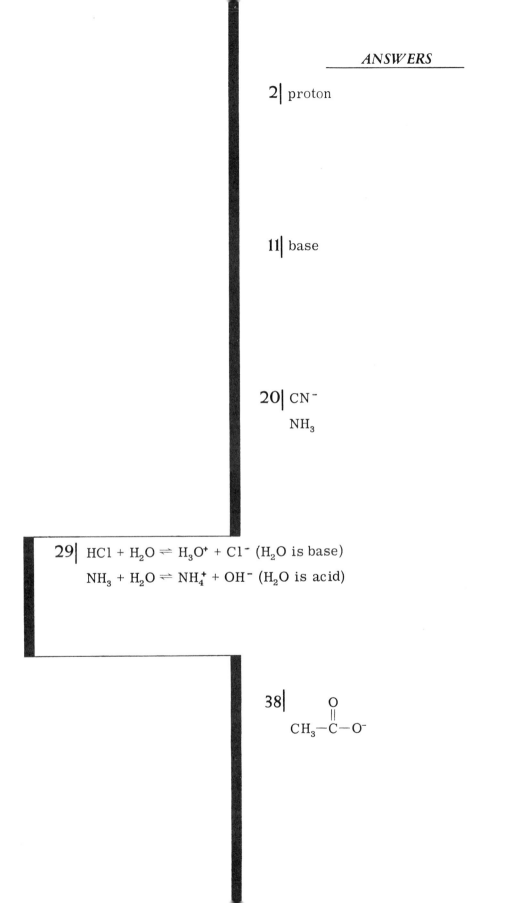

2| proton

11| base

20| CN⁻
   NH₃

29| HCl + H₂O ⇌ H₃O⁺ + Cl⁻ (H₂O is base)
   NH₃ + H₂O ⇌ NH₄⁺ + OH⁻ (H₂O is acid)

38|
$$CH_3-\overset{\overset{\displaystyle O}{\|}}{C}-O^-$$

4| Therefore, free H^+ ions are not found in a solution. If formed, they would immediately react with adjacent molecules that have

a pair of . . . . available for sharing.

13| In the gas phase, neutral molecules of HNO_3 exist. The reaction that takes place when neutral molecules of gaseous HNO_3 are

dissolved in water is $HNO_3 + H_2O \rightarrow$ . . . . $+ NO_3^-$.

22| Removal of a proton from an acid produces the conjugate base of the acid. Addition of a proton to a base produces the . . . . . .

. . . .

31| Of the four hydrogen atoms in the acetic acid molecule

$$CH_3-\overset{\overset{\displaystyle O}{\displaystyle \|}}{C}-OH$$ only the one on the oxygen atom can be transferred fairly readily to a base. The remaining acetate ion would be

drawn . . . .

40| No reaction occurs when sodium chloride is added to water because neither Na^+ nor Cl^- is a strong enough . . . . to remove a proton from the H_2O molecules.

3| H : H

H : Ö :

H

12| proton (or hydrogen ion)

$2H_2O$

21| OH⁻

H_2O

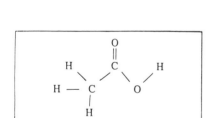

30| proton

H_2O

39| weak

NH_3

strong

5| In solution, protons can be transferred from a molecule or an ion in which they share a . . . . to another molecule, or ion, that has a free . . . .

14| If ammonia gas is dissolved in water, the reaction at the right occurs to an appreciable extent. In this reaction H_2O is the . . . . and NH_3 is the . . . .

23| In a reaction of the type $HA + B \rightarrow A^- + HB^+$, we say that HA is acting as a(n) . . . . and B as a(n) . . . .

32| Acetic acid $CH_3-\overset{\overset{O}{\|}}{C}-O-H$ in water is partially ionized. The reaction $CH_3-\overset{\overset{O}{\|}}{C}-OH + $ . . . . $\rightleftharpoons$ . . . . proceeds to some extent.

41| On the other hand, when the salt sodium acetate is dissolved in water, a reaction (called *hydrolysis*) occurs because the acetate ions $CH_3-\overset{\overset{O}{\|}}{C}-O^-$ are basic enough to abstract protons from H_2O molecules according to the equation

. . . . $\rightleftharpoons$ . . . .

$NH_3 + H_2O \rightarrow NH_4^+ + OH^-$

ANSWERS

4| electrons

13| H_3O^+

22| conjugate acid of the base

31| $CH_3-\overset{\overset{\displaystyle O}{\|}}{C}-O^-$

40| base

6| In solution, free H^+ ions do not occur, but they can be . . . . from one molecule to another.

15| In an aqueous solution of NaOH there are Na^+ and OH^- ions. In an aqueous solution of HCl there are . . . . ions and . . . . . . ions.

24| If this reaction ($HA + B \rightarrow A^- + HB^+$) were, in fact, found to proceed in the opposite direction, we would say that . . . . is acting as an acid and . . . . as a base.

33| In this reaction there are two bases, ... and . . . . . . , that are competing for the transferable protons.

42| As we saw earlier, if ammonia molecules are added to water an analogous reaction occurs, i.e., ... $\rightleftharpoons$ . . . .

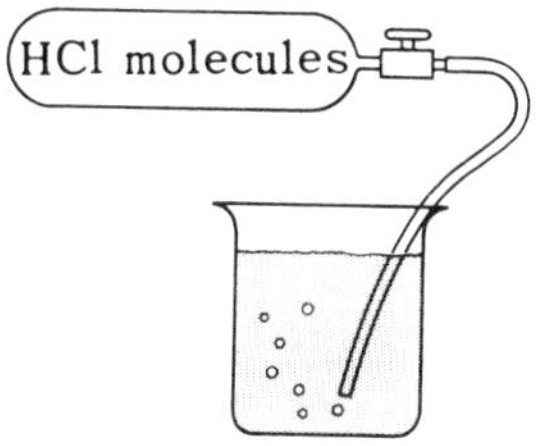

HCl molecules

5| pair of electrons

pair of electrons

14| acid

base

23| acid

base

32| $+ H_2O \rightleftharpoons CH_3-\overset{\overset{\textstyle O}{\|}}{C}-O^- + H_3O^+$

41| $CH_3-\overset{\overset{\textstyle O}{\|}}{C}-O^- + H_2O \rightleftharpoons$

$CH_3-\overset{\overset{\textstyle O}{\|}}{C}-OH + OH^-$

7| According to Brönsted's definition of acids and bases, an acid is a substance that can donate a proton and a base is a substance that can . . . .

16| The proton-transfer reaction that occurs when solutions of NaOH and HCl are mixed is $H_3O^+ + OH^- \rightarrow$ . . . . , and we see that the acid and the base in HCl and NaOH solutions are actually . . . . and . . . . , respectively.

25| H_2SO_4 tends to donate both its hydrogens to water molecules. The following steps can be written for the reaction of H_2SO_4 with water:

$$H_2SO_4 + H_2O \rightarrow HSO_4^- + H_3O^+$$
$$HSO_4^- + H_2O \rightarrow \text{. . . . .}$$

34| Since aqueous solutions of acetic acid contain some H_3O^+ and some $CH_3-\overset{\overset{O}{\|}}{C}-OH$, we can say that the molecule . . . . . . and the ion . . . . have about the same base strength.

43| When the salt ammonium chloride is added to water, some of the NH_4^+ ions will donate protons to water molecules. Therefore, H_3O^+ is present in an aqueous solution of ammonium chloride as a result of the hydrolysis reaction . . . .

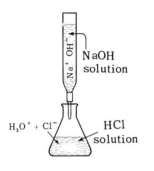

6| transferred

15| H_3O^+

Cl$^-$

24| HB$^+$

A$^-$

33| $CH_3-\overset{\overset{\displaystyle O}{\|}}{C}-O^-$

H_2O

42| $NH_3 + H_2O \rightleftharpoons NH_4^+ + OH^-$

8| When the gas HCl is dissolved in water, the reaction HCl + $H_2O \rightarrow$ $Cl^- + H_3O^+$ occurs. HCl is acting as a(n) . . . . and H_2O as a(n) . . . .

17| When a molecule acts as a base it . . . . a proton. Some molecules can accept protons more readily than others and are therefore *stronger* bases. Protons are easily . . . . from one base to another base of equal or greater strength.

26| In the first reaction H_2SO_4 is the acid, and . . . . is its conjugate base. In the second reaction HSO_4^- is the acid, and . . . . is its conjugate base.

35| On the other hand, the reaction HCl + $H_2O \rightarrow Cl^- + H_3O^+$ proceeds completely to the right and, of the two bases, ... and . . . . , which compete for the proton, the stronger base is . . . .

44| According to the Brönsted definition of acids and bases, a molecule or ion acts as an acid if it . . . . and as a base if it . . . .

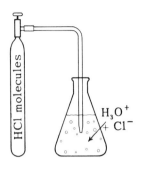

7 | accept a proton

16 | $2H_2O$

H_3O^+

OH^-

25 | $SO_4^= + H_3O^+$

34 | H_2O

$$CH_3-\overset{\overset{\textstyle O}{\|}}{C}-O^-$$

43 | $NH_4^+ + H_2O \rightleftharpoons NH_3 + H_3O^+$

9| The H_3O^+ ion is called the hydronium (or hydroxonium) ion. It is formed by the transfer of a proton (H^+) from an acid molecule to

a . . . . molecule.

(*return to page* 57)

18| When the species formed by the addition of a proton to one base donates the proton to another base, the former species acts as

an . . . . This acid is known as the *conjugate acid* of the original base.

(*return to page* 57)

27| Of the species H_2SO_4, HSO_4^-, and $SO_4^=$, which can act most easily both as an acid and as a base? . . . .

(*return to page* 57)

36| A strong acid readily gives up a proton; it follows that its conjugate base does not tend to . . . . a proton and is therefore

a . . . . base.

(*return to page* 57)

8| acid

base

17| accepts

transferred (or donated)

26| HSO_4^-

$SO_4^=$

35| Cl^-

H_2O

H_2O

44| donates a proton

accepts a proton

(*turn to page* 66)

NOW that acids and bases have been defined and the proton-transfer reactions that are most often encountered have been described, you can deal with the quantities of acids and bases that react with one another. In the following section this general background material will be used in studies of the stoichiometry of acid-base reactions that occur in solution. The concept of normality, which is useful in quantitative studies of acid-base reactions, will be introduced.

A typical problem arising from quantitative acid-base studies is this:

A 25.0-ml sample of Ba(OH)$_2$ solution required 37.2 ml of 0.110 N sulfuric acid for complete reaction. What was the normality of the hydroxide solution?

45| When aqueous solutions of HCl and NaOH are mixed, the reaction may be written HCl + NaOH $\rightarrow$ NaCl + H_2O. The actual, "net," reaction is H_3O^+ + ... $\rightarrow$ . . . .

5 | What volume of 0.25-M NaOH solution would be necessary to provide 0.050 mole of OH^-? . . . .

57| One molecule of the acid H_3PO_4 can transfer 3 protons to a base. One mole of H_3PO_4 is . . . . . equivalents of H_3PO_4.

63| In 2.5 liters of 0.20 N NaOH there is . . . . equivalent of NaOH.

69| Since each equivalent of any acid reacts with an equivalent of any base, the amounts required for complete reaction are related by the equation $V_1 N_1$ = ...

50| 0.050

56| $\frac{1}{2}$

62| VN (i.e., $V \times N$)

68| $V_1 N_1$
$V_2 N_2$

46| Each mole of HCl furnishes . . . . . mole of H_3O^+ in solution. Hence . . . . . mole of OH^- is required for complete reaction.

52| In 0.50 liter of 0.10 M H_2SO_4 there is . . . . mole(s) of H_2SO_4 or . . . . mole(s) of H_3O^+.

58| The amount of base that can accept 1 mole of protons is an *equivalent* of the base. One equivalent of NaOH is . . . . . mole(s) of NaOH.

64| In the reaction $H_3O^+ + OH^- \rightarrow 2H_2O$, each mole of OH^- reacts with . . . . . mole of H_3O^+.

70| A 0.500-liter sample of 0.100N acid contains . . . . equivalent. If this sample of acid is titrated with a 0.200-N base solution, the volume of base required for complete reaction will be . . . . liter(s).

$H_3O^+ + OH^- \rightarrow 2H_2O$

ANSWERS

45 $OH^- \rightarrow 2H_2O$

51 $0.050/0.25 = 0.20$ liter

57 3

63 $(2.5)(0.20) = 0.50$

69 V_2N_2

47| When aqueous solutions of H_2SO_4 and NaOH are mixed, the re-
action may be written $H_2SO_4 + 2NaOH \rightarrow Na_2SO_4 + 2H_2O$ or, to
show what is actually happening, $2H_3O^+$ + ... $\rightarrow$ . . . .

53| Reaction with 0.10 mole H_3O^+ requires . . . . . . mole(s) of
OH^-.

59| One mole of $Ca(OH)_2$ can furnish 2 moles of OH^- in solution. A
mole of $Ca(OH)_2$ is . . . . . equivalent(s).

65| An equivalent of acid will produce . . . . . mole of H_3O^+ in solu-
tion. An equivalent of base will produce . . . . . mole of OH^- in
solution.

71| A 25.0-ml sample of $Ba(OH)_2$ solution required 37.2 ml of 0.110-N
sulfuric acid solution for complete reaction. The normality of
the hydroxide solution was . . . .; the 25.0-ml sample con-
tained . . . . . . moles of $Ba(OH)_2$.

ANSWERS

46| 1

1

52| 0.050

0.10

58| 1

64| 1

70| 0.0500

0.250

48| Each mole of H_2SO_4 can produce . . . . . moles of H_3O^+ in solution; . . . . . moles of NaOH are required for complete reaction.

54| Since some acid molecules may transfer more than 1 proton to a base, the number of moles of protons available may be

. . . . than the number of moles of acid.

60| A 1-*normal* (*N*) solution of an acid or base contains *one* equivalent per liter of solution. One liter of a 0.5-*N* solution of HCl contains

. . . . . . equivalent of HCl.

66| One equivalent of any acid will react with . . . . . equivalent of any base.

72| Sodium carbonate (Na_2CO_3) reacts with H_3O^+ according to the equations $CO_3^= + 2H_3O^+ \rightarrow H_2CO_3 + 2H_2O$ and $H_2CO_3 \rightarrow H_2O + CO_2$. What volume of 0.100-*N* H_2SO_4 solution will be required for complete reaction with 0.492 g of Na_2CO_3? . . . .

At. wt.	
Na	23.0
C	12.0
O	16.0

ANSWERS

47 | $2OH^- \rightarrow 4H_2O$

53 | 0.10

59 | 2

65 | 1

1

71 | $N = (37.2)(0.110)/25.0 = 0.164$

equivalents of $Ba(OH)_2 = VN$
$= (0.0250)(0.164) = 0.00410$

moles of $Ba(OH)_2 = 0.00410/2$
$= 0.00205$

49| In 0.50 liter of 0.10 M HCl there is . . . . mole of HCl or
. . . . mole of H_3O^+.

55| An *equivalent* of an acid is defined as the amount of acid that will
transfer 1 mole of protons to a base. An equivalent of HCl is . . .
mole of HCl.

61| A 0.6-N solution contains . . . . of acid or base per liter
of solution.

67| In 0.15 liter of 0.20 N NaOH there is(are) . . . . equivalent(s)
which will react with . . . . equivalent of HCl, or with
. . . . equivalent of H_2SO_4.

48| 2

2

54| greater

N = abbreviation for *normal*

60| 0.5

66| 1

72| equivalents of Na_2CO_3 = $\left(\dfrac{0.492\ g}{106\ g/mole}\right)$ (2 eq/mole) = 0.00928

equivalents of H_2SO_4 = VN

V = 0.00928/0.100 = 0.0928 liter

(*turn to page* 73)

50| For reaction with this 0.050 mole of H_3O^+, ... mole of OH^- is required.

(*return to page* 67)

56| An equivalent of H_2SO_4 is . . . . . mole(s) of H_2SO_4.

(*return to page* 67)

62| The number of equivalents in V liters of an N-normal solution is

. . . . . .

(*return to page* 67)

68| V_1 liters of N_1 normal acid solution contains . . . . equivalents.

V_2 liters of N_2 normal base contains . . . . equivalents.

(*return to page* 67)

49| 0.50(.10) = 0.050
  0.050

55| 1

61| 0.6 equivalent

67| 0.030
  0.030
  0.030

THE concept of acids and bases is a very important one in chemistry, and here you have learned some of the characteristics of acids and bases, defined according to their ability to donate or accept protons. There are, it should be mentioned, broader definitions of acids and bases. Moreover, in this introductory material, only aqueous systems were considered. Further interesting features of acid-base reactions are revealed when other solvents are used.

What you have learned in this chapter will allow you to write the equations for the reactions between many reagents on the basis of their classification as acids or bases, and, moreover, with the use of normality you can do acid-base stoichiometric calculations in a very convenient way.

In Chapter 6 you will again consider reactions between acids and bases, but then you will see how these systems are treated when the reactions do not proceed completely from reactants to products but instead reach some intermediate equilibrium state.

CHAPTER FIVE

Balancing

Redox

Equations

THE ability to balance chemical equations is essential to an understanding of the heart of chemistry—the chemical reaction. Balanced equations show the relative number of ions and molecules that are involved in a chemical reaction and, therefore, allow the important calculations of the weights of reagents that react with each other, or the weight of products that might be formed, to be made. Balanced equations also provide the first step for quantitative treatments of chemical equilibria and electrochemistry, to name but two additional general areas where balanced chemical equations are used.

Many simple equations can often be balanced by inspection, but equations involving oxidation and reduction are frequently difficult to balance so directly. An easy system for balancing such equations is based on the familiar oxidation number concept. On completion of this chapter you will be able to balance any reaction involving oxidation and reduction by this method, once you know what the reactants and products are. It is assumed, in this chapter on the balancing of oxidation-reduction equations, that you have already learned how to assign oxidation numbers to the atoms of an ion or a molecule. Here is a brief review of the principal features of the assignment of oxidation numbers, given to remind you of this background material.

You will recall that oxidation numbers provide a "bookkeeping" procedure for counting the electrons that can be associated with, or assigned to, each atom of the molecule or ion on the basis of its relative electro-negativity. An oxidation number of zero implies that the atom in a molecule or ion is assigned the same number of electrons as it has in the free atom. Negative values of oxidation numbers correspond to a greater number of electrons than in the neutral atom, whereas positive values correspond to a smaller number of electrons.

Oxidation numbers can be assigned to atoms in molecules or ions on the basis of six rules. You should already have learned these rules. They are:

1. The atoms in an element, such as He, H_2, O_2, Cl_2, S_8, Zn, have an oxidation number of *zero*.

2. Simple ions, such as Cl^-, Zn^{++}, have oxidation numbers equal to the charge on the ion.

3. Except for O_2, O_3 (ozone), OF_2, peroxides, and the superoxides (KO_2, RbO_2, CsO_2), the oxidation number of the oxygen atom in any molecule or ion is -2. (In peroxides the oxygen atom is assigned the oxidation number -1 and in the superoxides $-\frac{1}{2}$).

4. The alkali metals, except as the element or when combined with each other, have an oxidation number of $+1$. The alkaline earth metals form only $+2$ ions and, similarly, have an oxidation number of $+2$.

5. Except for H_2 and the metal hydrides such as NaH, the oxidation number of the hydrogen atom in any molecule or ion is $+1$. (In the metal hydrides hydrogen is assigned the value -1.)

6. The sum of the oxidation numbers of all the atoms in a molecule must be zero, and this sum for an ion must be equal to the charge on the ion. Thus for CH_4, since each H has an oxidation number of $+1$, the carbon atom must have the value -4 to give a total value for the molecule of zero. For the sulfate ion $SO_4^=$, since each oxygen has an oxidation number of -2, the sulfur atom in $SO_4^=$ must have an oxidation number of $+6$ so that the total for the ion is -2, equal to the charge on the ion.

As a test that you know and understand these rules and can assign oxidation numbers, and therefore are ready to proceed with this chapter, assign oxidation numbers to the atoms in each of the following examples:

(1) N_2 (4) H_2CO_3 (7) HCl   (10) MnO_2
(2) NH_3 (5) $CO_3^=$ (8) HClO   (11) Na_2SO_3
(3) H_2O_2 (6) V_2O_3 (9) $KMnO_4$ (12) $Cr_2O_7^=$

(*answers on page* 76)

1. N has oxid. no. of zero (rule 1).
2. H has oxid. no. of +1 (rule 5) and, to make the total of the oxidation numbers of the molecule equal to zero, N must have oxid. no. −3.
3. This is a peroxide, hydrogen peroxide. Each H has oxid. no. of +1; each O has oxid. no. −1.
4. Each H has oxid. no. +1; each O has oxid. no. −2. In order that the total for the molecule comes out to zero, the carbon atom must be assigned the value +4.
5. Each O is −2, and C must be +4 to make the total for the ion equal to the ion's charge.
6. Each O is −2 and each vanadium atom must be +3 to give a total for the molecule of zero.
7. Since H is +1, Cl must be −1.
8. Since H is +1 and O is −2, Cl must be +1.
9. Since each O is −2 and K is +1, Mn must be +7 to give a total of zero for the molecule.
10. Since each O is −2, Mn must be +4.
11. Since each O is −2 and each Na is +1, S must be +4.
12. Since each O is −2, each Cr must be +6 for the total of the oxidation numbers to be equal to the charge on the ion.

1| The word *redox*, which describes a reaction in which electrons are transferred from one substance to another, is derived from the words . . .duction and . . .dation.

10| Write an equation to represent the oxidation of two chloride ions to Cl_2: . . . .

19| Is the equation balanced with respect to charge? . . . .

28| If the reaction occurs in aqueous solution, H_2O molecules may be involved as reactants or products. Balance the hydrogen atoms in the equation by adding an appropriate number of H_2O molecules. . . . .

37| In basic solution, $HV_6O_{17}^{3-}$ may be converted to elemental V. To balance the half-reaction we first . . . .

Do this: . . . .

9| −1

0

oxidation

18| 0   −2

$S_8 + 16e \rightarrow 8S^=$

$$
\boxed{
\begin{array}{l}
{}^{+5} \qquad\qquad\quad {}^{+2} \\
NO_3^- + 3e + 4H^+ \rightarrow NO
\end{array}
}
$$

27| the number of atoms of H and O

36| left: 8 O

right: 8 O

yes

2| Oxidation numbers (ox. no.) help us keep track of the number of electrons associated with an atom or ion. Since in redox reactions . . . . are transferred from one reagent to another, the . . . . of some of the atoms of the reagents change.

11| Such an equation is known as a *half-reaction*. Half-reactions show only reduction or oxidation and show, as part of the balanced equation, the electrons lost or gained by an atom. Write the half-reaction for the reduction of Fe^{3+} to Fe: . . . .

20| To balance the equation for the half-reaction $NO_3^- \rightarrow NO$, we first assign . . . . , as: . . . .

29| If the equation is now also balanced with respect to O atoms, the equation is completely balanced. Check this.

38| The next step is to . . . . The equation becomes . . . .

ANSWERS

1| re

oxi

10| $$\overset{-1}{2Cl^-} \rightarrow \overset{0}{Cl_2} + 2e$$

19| yes $\begin{pmatrix} \text{left:} & -16 \\ \text{right:} & -16 \end{pmatrix}$

28| $$\overset{+5}{NO_3^-} + 3e + 4H^+ \rightarrow \overset{+2}{NO} + 2H_2O$$

37| assign oxidation numbers

$$\overset{+1}{H}\overset{+5}{V_6}\overset{-2}{O_{17}^{3-}} \rightarrow \overset{0}{V}$$

3| If a reagent loses electrons its oxidation number is increased. In the example $Cu^+ - e \rightarrow Cu^{++}$, the oxidation number of copper has increased from . . . . . to . . . . . ; Cu^+ has been oxidized to Cu^{++}.

12| The equation for a half-reaction is balanced if, on each side of the equation, there are the same number of electrons, the same number of atoms of each element, and the same net charge. In the preceding equation the net charge of each side is . . . .

21| The element undergoing reduction is . . . .

30| Tabulate the steps that have been taken to balance the half-reaction treated in the preceding items:
(a) Assign oxidation numbers and balance the number of atoms of the element involved.
(b) . . . .
(c) . . . .
(d) . . . .
(e) Check by seeing that O atoms are balanced.

39| The third step is that of . . . . ; Cu^+ has . . . . . . The equation becomes . . . .

2| electrons

   oxidation numbers

11|
$$\overset{+3}{Fe^{3+}} + 3e \rightarrow \overset{0}{Fe}$$

20| oxidation numbers

$$\overset{+5\ -2}{NO_3^-} \rightarrow \overset{+2\ -2}{NO}$$

29| left: 3 O

   right: 3 O

38| balance V atoms

$$\overset{+5}{HV_6O_{17}^{3-}} \rightarrow \overset{0}{6V}$$

4| It is customary to write equations showing the *addition* of electrons to the appropriate side and to place the oxidation number of each atom above its symbol. Rewrite the equation for the oxidation of Cu^+ in this way: . . . .

13| To begin balancing the equation for the half-reaction $Cl_2 \rightarrow Cl^-$, first assign oxidation numbers to the reagents. . . . .
. . . .

22| Since this equation is balanced with respect to the number of atoms of the element being reduced, the next step is to add electrons to the appropriate side. The equation becomes . . . .
. . . .

31| In acidic solution $S_2O_3^=$ can be converted to $SO_4^=$. Assign oxidation numbers in the half-reaction $S_2O_3^= \rightarrow SO_4^=$. . . . .
. . . . .

40| The fourth step is that of . . . . Since the reaction is done in basic solution, the equation becomes . . . . . .
. . . .

$$Cu^+ - e \rightarrow Cu^{++}$$

$$\begin{matrix} +5 & +2 \\ NO_3^- & \rightarrow NO \end{matrix}$$

ANSWERS

3| +1

+2

12| left: $+3 + (-3) = 0$

right: 0

21| nitrogen

30| (b) Add electrons to balance
the change in oxidation
number.
(c) Add H^+ to balance charge.
(d) Add H_2O to balance number
of H atoms.

39| balancing electrons

$$30e + \overset{+5}{H}V_6O_{17}^{3-} \rightarrow 6\overset{0}{V}$$

5| Reduction of a reagent corresponds to an increase in the number of electrons assigned to an atom of the reagent, therefore to a(n) . . . .crease in the oxidation number.

14| Next, balance the number of atoms of the element being oxidized or reduced: . . . .

23| The net charge on the left is . . . . ; on the right . . . . . .

32| Is this an oxidation or a reduction half-reaction? . . . .

41| The fifth step is that of balancing . . . . The equation becomes . . . .

4|
$$\overset{+1}{Cu^+} \rightarrow \overset{+2}{Cu^{++}} + e$$

13|
$$\overset{0}{Cl_2} \rightarrow \overset{-1}{Cl^-}$$

22|
$$\overset{+5}{NO_3^-} + 3e \rightarrow \overset{+2}{NO}$$

31|
$$\overset{+2-2}{S_2O_3^=} \rightarrow \overset{+6-2}{SO_4^=}$$

40| balancing charge

$$30e + \overset{+5}{HV_6O_{17}^{3-}} \rightarrow \overset{0}{6V} + 33OH^-$$

6 | Write the equation, including oxidation numbers, for the reduc-
tion of Cu^{++} to Cu^{+}. . . . .

15 | Since each of the two Cl atoms shows a decrease in oxidation
number from . . . . . to . . . . . , a total of . . . . . electrons must
be picked up by Cl_2. When these are shown on the . . . . . side of
the equation, the equation becomes . . . .

24 | The fact that the charge is not equal on the two sides of the
equation implies that some additional charged species is involved in the half-reaction. If the reaction proceeds in basic
aqueous solution, we generally assume OH^- ions might be involved. Add OH^- ions to balance the charges: . . . .
. . . . . .

33 | Balance this half-reaction with respect to the element being
oxidized and add electrons to the appropriate side: . . . .
. . . .

42 | Check the equation. Is it balanced? . . . .

$$\boxed{\begin{array}{c} +5 \qquad\qquad +2 \\ NO_3^- + 3e \;\to\; NO \end{array}}$$

$$\boxed{\begin{array}{c} +2-2 \quad +6-2 \\ S_2O_3^{=} \;\to\; SO_4^{=} \end{array}}$$

5| de

14| $\overset{0}{Cl_2} \to 2\overset{-1}{Cl^-}$

23| $-1 + (-3) = -4$
O

32| oxidation

41| H atoms

$$30e \;+\; \overset{+5}{HV_6O_{17}^{3-}} + 16H_2O \;\to\; 6\overset{0}{V}$$
$$+\; 33OH^-$$

7| The relation between oxidation and reduction and the loss or gain of electrons by an element is as follows: When an element loses electrons it is said to be . . . . , and conversely when it gains electrons, it is said to be . . . .

16| This equation is balanced with respect to atoms and electrons. What is the net charge on each side? . . . .

25| If the half-reaction at the right occurs in acidic solution, H^+ (which is usually written rather than H_3O^+) is the reagent that is generally assumed to be involved. Add H^+ ions to balance the charges: . . . .

34| Since this reaction occurs in acidic solution, H^+ ions are added to balance the . . . . The equation becomes . . . .

$$\begin{matrix} +5 & & +2 \\ NO_3^- + 3e & \to & NO \end{matrix}$$

6| $\overset{+2}{Cu^{++}} + e \to \overset{+1}{Cu^+}$

15| 0

−1

two

left

$\overset{0}{Cl_2} + 2e \to 2\overset{-1}{Cl^-}$

24| $\overset{+5}{NO_3^-} + 3e \to \overset{+2}{NO} + 4OH^-$

33| $\overset{+2}{S_2O_3^=} \to 2\overset{+6}{SO_4^=} + 8e$

42| yes

(*turn to page* 86)

8| Similarly, oxidation corresponds to a(n) . . . . in oxidation number; reduction corresponds to a(n) . . . . in oxidation number.

17| Balance the equation for the half-reaction $S_8 \rightarrow S^=$ by first assigning oxidation numbers and balancing atoms: . . . .

26| For reactions that occur in acidic solution, equations are balanced by adding H^+. For reactions occurring in basic solution, ... ions are added to balance charge.

35| The equation is now unbalanced with respect to . . . . , so that . . . . is added to the . . . . side. . . . .

7| oxidized

reduced

16| left: -2

right: -2

25| $\overset{+5}{NO_3^-} + 3e + 4H^+ \rightarrow \overset{+2}{NO}$

34| charge

$\overset{+2}{S_2O_3^=} \rightarrow 2\overset{+6}{SO_4^=} + 8e + 10H^+$

9| When Cl⁻ ions are converted to Cl_2, the oxidation number of chlorine increases from . . . . . to . . . . . . Is this conversion a reduction or an oxidation? . . . .

(return to page 77)

18| Next, add electrons to the appropriate side of the equation.

. . . .

(return to page 77)

27| The equation at right is balanced with respect to electrons and charge. It is not balanced with respect to . . . .

. . . . . .

(return to page 77)

36| Check the number of oxygen atoms on both sides. Is the equation completely balanced? . . . .

(return to page 77)

$$\overset{+5}{NO_3^-} + 3e + 4H^+ \rightarrow \overset{+2}{NO}$$

ANSWERS

8 | increase

decrease

17 | $\overset{0}{S_8} \rightarrow \overset{-2}{8S^=}$

26 | OH^-

35 | H and O atoms

H_2O

left

$$5H_2O + \overset{+2}{S_2O_3^=} \rightarrow \overset{+6}{2SO_4^=} + 8e + 10H^+$$

A S soon as you have learned how to balance equations for half-reactions, the problem of balancing equations for over-all reactions becomes almost trivial. The over-all reaction is a combination of two half-reactions, one of which is an oxidation half-reaction that produces electrons; the other is a reduction half-reaction that uses up these electrons. You must recognize the two half-reactions (after assignment of oxidation numbers), balance the half-reactions separately, and finally combine them so that the number of electrons produced in one half-reaction equals the number consumed in the other.

43| Metallic silver will dissolve in nitric acid to give Ag^+ and NO. To begin balancing the equation for this reaction, assign oxidation numbers to the atoms. . . . .

46| Balance this half-reaction. . . . .

49| Another example is the reaction of copper with nitric acid: $Cu + NO_3^- \rightarrow Cu^{++} + NO$. Assign oxidation numbers to the atoms you expect are involved in oxidation and reduction. The two half-reactions are:

(oxidation) . . . .

(reduction) . . . .

52| The addition step is

. . . .

. . . .

. . . .

55| In this reaction, part of the Cl_2 is reduced to . . . . and part is oxidized to . . . .

$Ag + NO_3^- \rightarrow Ag^+ + NO$

ANSWERS

45 nitrogen

$$\overset{+5}{NO_3^-} \rightarrow \overset{+2}{NO}$$

48 $3Ag + NO_3^- + 4H^+ \rightarrow 3Ag^+ + NO + 2H_2O$

$Cu \rightarrow Cu^{++} + 2e$
$4H^+ + 3e + NO_3^- \rightarrow NO + 2H_2O$

51 three

two

54 $\overset{0}{Cl_2} \rightarrow \overset{-1}{Cl^-} + \overset{+1+1-2}{HClO}$

44| The element undergoing oxidation is . . . . . . The easily

balanced half-reaction therefore is . . . .

47| In order to obtain the balanced total equation, the half-reactions must be added so that the electrons of each half-reaction cancel. In order to have this happen for the two half-reactions at right, the

oxidation equation must be multiplied by . . . .

50| After the equations for the half-reactions are separately bal-anced, they are:

. . . .

. . . .

53| Check the total equation. Is it balanced with respect to both

charge and atoms? . . . .

56| The two balanced half-reactions are

$$2e + Cl_2 \rightarrow 2Cl^-$$
$$2H_2O + Cl_2 \rightarrow 2HClO + 2e + 2H^+$$

They are combined to give the total balanced equation: . . . .

. . . .

ANSWERS

43| $\overset{0}{Ag} + \overset{+5-2}{NO_3^-} \rightarrow \overset{+1}{Ag^+} + \overset{+2-2}{NO}$

$Ag \rightarrow Ag^+ + e$
$NO_3^- + 3e + 4H^+ \rightarrow NO + 2H_2O$

46| $\overset{+5}{NO_3^-} + 3e + 4H^+ \rightarrow \overset{+2}{NO} + 2H_2O$
(see item 20ff for steps)

49| $\overset{0}{Cu} + \overset{+5}{NO_3^-} \rightarrow \overset{+2}{Cu^{++}} + \overset{+2}{NO}$

(oxidation) $Cu \rightarrow Cu^{++}$
(reduction) $NO_3^- \rightarrow NO$

52|
$$\begin{array}{r} 3\,Cu \rightarrow 3Cu^{++} + 6e \\ 8H^+ + 6e + 2NO_3^- \rightarrow 2NO + 4H_2O \\ \hline 3Cu + 8H^+ + 2NO_3^- \rightarrow 3Cu^{++} + 2NO + 4H_2O \end{array}$$

55| Cl^-

HClO

45| The element undergoing reduction is . . . . The half-

reaction is . . . .

(return to page 87)

48| Addition of the two half-reactions gives the total equation:

. . . .

(return to page 87)

51| In order for the electrons to cancel when the two equations are

added, the oxidation half-reaction must be multiplied by . . . . . .

and the reduction half-reaction by . . . .

(return to page 87)

54| Assign oxidation numbers to the atoms in the reaction
$Cl_2 \rightarrow Cl^- + HClO$.

(acidic solution)

(return to page 87)

$$\begin{array}{cccc} 0 & +5-2 & +1 & +2-2 \\ Ag + NO_3^- & \to & Ag^+ + NO \end{array}$$

44 Ag

$$\begin{array}{cc} 0 & +1 \\ Ag \to Ag^+ + e \end{array}$$

$$3Ag \to 3Ag^+ + 3e$$
$$NO_3^- + 3e + 4H^+ \to NO + 2H_2O$$

47 three

50 $Cu \to Cu^{++} + 2e$

$$4H^+ + 3e + NO_3^- \to NO + 2H_2O$$

53 yes

56 $2H_2O + 2Cl_2 \to 2Cl^- + 2HClO + 2H^+$

or

$$H_2O + Cl_2 \to Cl^- + HClO + H^+$$

(*turn to page* 90)

$\mathbf{A}$ DDITIONAL examples of redox equations are given on the following three pages. Balance each equation, writing down each step for both half-reactions, on these pages. The steps in balancing each equation appear on the page following the question. Use the summary below if necessary, but practice on these equations until you can balance them without help.

Summary of Steps for Balancing Redox Equations

1. Write down the main reactants and products.
2. Assign oxidation numbers.
3. Separate the oxidation and reduction half-reactions.
4. Balance the half-reactions with respect to
    a. the number of atoms of the element undergoing oxidation or reduction.
    b. electrons by adding electrons to the electron-deficient side of the equation.
    c. charge by adding H^+ ions or OH^- ions.
    d. H and O atoms by adding H_2O.
5. Multiply the half-reactions by appropriate numbers so that, when they are added, the electrons cancel.
6. Add the half-reactions and check for balance.

1 $H_2S + Cr_2O_7^= \rightarrow S + Cr^{3+}$ (acid solution)

4 $NO_2 \rightarrow NO_3^- + NO$ (acid solution)

3| $Zn + NO_3^- \rightarrow Zn^{++} + NH_4^+$ (acid solution)

$\quad 0 \quad\quad +2 \quad\quad\quad +5 \quad\quad -3$

$Zn \rightarrow Zn^{++} \quad\quad\quad NO_3^- \rightarrow NH_4^+$

$Zn \rightarrow Zn^{++} + 2e \quad\quad NO_3^- + 8e \rightarrow NH_4^+$

$\quad\quad\quad\quad\quad\quad\quad\quad NO_3^- + 10H^+ + 8e \rightarrow NH_4^+$

$\quad\quad\quad\quad\quad\quad\quad\quad NO_3^- + 10H^+ + 8e \rightarrow NH_4^+ + 3H_2O$

$$4Zn \rightarrow 4Zn^{++} + 8e$$
$$\underline{NO_3^- + 10H^+ + 8e \rightarrow NH_4^+ + 3H_2O}$$
$$4Zn + NO_3^- + 10H^+ \rightarrow 4Zn^{++} + NH_4^+ + 3H_2O$$

6| $Al + OH^- \rightarrow Al(OH)_4^- + H_2$ (basic solution)

$\quad 0 \quad +3 \quad\quad\quad\quad\quad\quad\quad +1 \quad\quad 0$

$Al \rightarrow Al(OH)_4^- \quad\quad\quad\quad OH^- \rightarrow H_2$

$Al \rightarrow Al(OH)_4^- + 3e \quad\quad 2OH^- + 2e \rightarrow H_2$

$Al + 4OH^- \rightarrow Al(OH)_4^- + 3e \quad 2OH^- + 2e \rightarrow H_2 + 4OH^-$

$\quad\quad\quad\quad\quad\quad\quad\quad\quad\quad or \quad\quad 2e \rightarrow H_2 + 2OH^-$

$\quad\quad\quad\quad\quad\quad\quad\quad\quad\quad 2H_2O + 2e \rightarrow H_2 + 2OH^-$

$$2Al + 8OH^- \rightarrow 2Al(OH)_4^- + 6e$$
$$\underline{6H_2O + 6e \rightarrow 3H_2 + 6OH^-}$$
$$2Al + 6H_2O + 2OH^- \rightarrow 2Al(OH)_4^- + 3H_2 \quad$$ *(turn to page 94)*

$2|$ $ClO^- + CrO_2^- \rightarrow Cl^- + CrO_4^=$ (basic solution)

$5|$ $MnO_4^- + H_2O_2 \rightarrow Mn^{++} + O_2$ (acid solution)

1| $H_2S + Cr_2O_7^= \rightarrow S + Cr^{3+}$ (acid solution)

$$\begin{array}{ll} -2 \quad 0 & +6 \qquad +3 \\ H_2S \rightarrow S & Cr_2O_7^= \rightarrow Cr^{3+} \\ H_2S \rightarrow S + 2e & Cr_2O_7^= + 6e \rightarrow 2Cr^{3+} \\ H_2S \rightarrow S + 2H^+ + 2e & Cr_2O_7^= + 14H^+ + 6e \rightarrow 2Cr^{3+} \\ & Cr_2O_7^= + 14H^+ + 6e \rightarrow 2Cr^{3+} + 7H_2O \end{array}$$

$$3H_2S \rightarrow 3S + 6H^+ + 6e$$
$$\underline{Cr_2O_7^= + 14H^+ + 6e \rightarrow 2Cr^{3+} + 7H_2O}$$
$$3H_2S + Cr_2O_7^= + 8H^+ \rightarrow 3S + 2Cr^{3+} + 7H_2O$$

4| $NO_2 \rightarrow NO_3^- + NO$ (acid solution)

$$\begin{array}{ll} +4 \qquad +5 & +4 \qquad +2 \\ NO_2 \rightarrow NO_3^- & NO_2 \rightarrow NO \\ NO_2 \rightarrow NO_3^- + e & NO_2 + 2e \rightarrow NO \\ NO_2 \rightarrow NO_3^- + 2H^+ + e & NO_2 + 2H^+ + 2e \rightarrow NO \\ NO_2 + H_2O \rightarrow NO_3^- + 2H^+ + e & NO_2 + 2H^+ + 2e \rightarrow NO + H_2O \end{array}$$

$$2NO_2 + 2H_2O \rightarrow 2NO_3^- + 4H^+ + 2e$$
$$\underline{NO_2 + 2H^+ + 2e \rightarrow NO + H_2O}$$
$$3NO_2 + H_2O \rightarrow 2NO_3^- + NO + 2H^+$$

3| $Zn + NO_3^- \rightarrow Zn^{++} + NH_4^+$ (acid solution)

(*return to page* 91)

6| $Al + OH^- \rightarrow Al(OH)_4^- + H_2$ (basic solution)

(*return to page* 91)

2 $ClO^- + CrO_2^- \rightarrow Cl^- + CrO_4^=$ (basic solution)

$\overset{+3}{CrO_2^-} \quad \overset{+6}{CrO_4^=}$ $\qquad\qquad\qquad \overset{+1}{ClO^-} \quad \overset{-1}{Cl^-}$

$CrO_2^- \rightarrow CrO_4^=$ $\qquad\qquad\qquad ClO^- \rightarrow Cl^-$

$CrO_2^- \rightarrow CrO_4^= + 3e$ $\qquad\qquad ClO^- + 2e \rightarrow Cl^-$

$CrO_2^- + 4OH^- \rightarrow CrO_4^= + 3e$ $\qquad ClO^- + 2e \rightarrow Cl^- + 2OH^-$

$CrO_2^- + 4OH^- \rightarrow CrO_4^= + 2H_2O + 3e \quad ClO^- + H_2O + 2e \rightarrow Cl^- + 2OH^-$

$$2CrO_2^- + 8OH^- \rightarrow 2CrO_4^= + 4H_2O + 6e$$
$$\underline{3ClO^- + 3H_2O + 6e \rightarrow 3Cl^- + 6OH^-}$$
$$2CrO_2^- + 3ClO^- + 2OH^- \rightarrow 2CrO_4^= + 3Cl^- + H_2O$$

5 $MnO_4^- + H_2O_2 \rightarrow Mn^{++} + O_2$ (acid solution)

$\overset{-1}{H_2O_2} \quad \overset{0}{O_2}$ $\qquad\qquad \overset{+7}{MnO_4^-} \quad \overset{+2}{Mn^{++}}$

$H_2O_2 \rightarrow O_2$ $\qquad\qquad\qquad MnO_4^- \rightarrow Mn^{++}$

$H_2O_2 \rightarrow O_2 + 2e$ $\qquad\qquad MnO_4^- + 5e \rightarrow Mn^{++}$

$H_2O_2 \rightarrow O_2 + 2H^+ + 2e \quad MnO_4^- + 8H^+ + 5e \rightarrow Mn^{++}$

$\qquad\qquad\qquad\qquad\qquad MnO_4^- + 8H^+ + 5e \rightarrow Mn^{++} + 4H_2O$

$$5H_2O_2 \rightarrow 5O_2 + 10H^+ + 10e$$
$$\underline{2MnO_4^- + 16H^+ + 10e \rightarrow 2Mn^{++} + 8H_2O}$$
$$5H_2O_2 + 2MnO_4^- + 6H^+ \rightarrow 5O_2 + 2Mn^{++} + 8H_2O$$

CHAPTER SIX

Equilibrium

Calculations

CHEMICAL reactions tend to proceed until they reach a state of equilibrium. For example, if $N_2O_4(g)$ is introduced into a container, dissociation to $NO_2(g)$ occurs, and the reaction $N_2O_4(g) \rightleftharpoons 2NO_2(g)$ continues until some definite fraction is converted to NO_2 and equilibrium is established. The concentrations of the reagents at equilibrium are related by an expression that, for this example, has the form $K = [NO_2]^2/[N_2O_4]$, K being the *equilibrium constant* for this reaction. (In later studies you will see that this is an approximation and is valid for *ideal* behavior in much the same way that the expression $PV = nRT$ is really valid only for *ideal* gases.)

It is assumed in this chapter that you know how to write the expression for the equilibrium constant for a reaction if the equation for the reaction is given. You will learn to use such equations to calculate the concentrations, at equilibrium, of reagents in various systems.

The first section of the chapter deals with the equilibria established by gases in a container having a fixed volume and temperature; the second section treats equilibria in solution.

A typical problem that you will learn to solve here is the following:

Calculate the equilibrium concentrations when 0.060 mole of PCl_5 and 0.020 mole of PCl_3 are allowed to come to equilibrium, according to the reaction $PCl_5(g) \rightleftharpoons PCl_3(g) + Cl_2(g)$ in a 4.7-liter container at 250°C. The equilibrium constant at this temperature is 0.042 mole/liter.

1| At 250°C, phosphorus pentachloride dissociates according to the equation at the right. If 1.0 mole of PCl_5 is introduced into a container at 250°C, at a later time there will be . .(less, .more) . than 1.0 mole of PCl_5 present.

12| According to the equation at the right, every mole of H_2O that dissociates produces . . . . . mole(s) of H_2 and . . . . . mole(s) of O_2.

23| The concentration results of the preceding item are usually indicated with the notation: $[HCl]$ = ...; $[H_2]$ = ...; and $[Cl_2]$ = ...

34| Using the expressions of the preceding item and the value of K at this temperature of 0.042, set up an expression that permits the calculation of x. . . . .

ANSWERS

$PCl_5(g) \rightleftharpoons PCl_3(g) + Cl_2(g)$

$2H_2O(g) \rightleftharpoons 2H_2(g) + O_2(g)$

11 $PCl_5(g) \rightleftharpoons PCl_3(g) + Cl_2(g)$

equal

22

$2HCl(g)$	$\rightleftharpoons$ $H_2(g)$	+ $Cl_2(g)$
2.86	1.00	0
1.30	1.00 + (1.56/2) = 1.78	0.78
0.101	0.138	0.060

$PCl_5(g) \rightleftharpoons PCl_3(g) + Cl_2(g)$

33 $PCl_5(g) \rightleftharpoons PCl_3(g) + Cl_2(g)$

$$\frac{1.00 - x}{5.0} \quad \frac{1.00 + x}{5.0} \quad \frac{x}{5.0}$$

2| Each mole of PCl_5 that dissociates produces . . . . . mole(s) of PCl_3 and . . . . . mole(s) of Cl_2.

13| If n moles of H_2O are heated until x moles have dissociated, the amounts of the three reagents present will be H_2O = ... moles; H_2 = ... moles; and O_2 = ... moles.

24| The square brackets around a chemical symbol indicate that the . . . . of the compound is being given and that the units are . . . . per . . . .

35| Solution of the quadratic gives x = 0.16. Complete the tabulation of the equilibrium amounts.

	Moles initially	Moles at equilibrium
PCl_5	1.00	
PCl_3	1.00	
Cl_2	0.0	

ANSWERS

$PCl_5(g) \rightleftharpoons PCl_3(g) + Cl_2(g)$

1 | less

$2H_2O(g) \rightleftharpoons 2H_2(g) + O_2(g)$

12 | 1

$\frac{1}{2}$

23 | 0.101

0.138

0.060

	$PCl_5(g)$	$\rightleftharpoons PCl_3(g)$	$+ Cl_2(g)$
equil. moles	$1.00 - x$	$1.00 + x$	x

34 | $0.042 = \frac{x(1.00 + x)}{5.0(1.00 - x)}$

3| As the reaction proceeds the number of moles of PCl_5 will . . . .-crease; the number of moles of PCl_3 will . . . . .crease.

14| If n moles of H_2O are heated until the system contains, as a result of dissociation, y moles of O_2, the amounts present will be

$O_2 = y$ moles; $H_2 = $ . . . . moles; and $H_2O = $ . . . . moles.

25| The equilibrium constant for the reaction at the right has the form

$K = $ . . . .

36| Check the calculations of the previous items by calculating the value of K from the results of the preceding item. (Recall that $K = 0.042$ was used to obtain these values.)

ANSWERS

$$PCl_5(g) \rightleftharpoons PCl_3(g) + Cl_2(g)$$

2 | 1

1

$$2H_2O(g) \rightleftharpoons 2H_2(g) + O_2(g)$$

13 | $n - x$

x

$x/2$

$$PCl_5(g) \rightleftharpoons PCl_3(g) + Cl_2(g)$$

24 | concentration

moles

liter

At equilibrium

$$[PCl_5] = \frac{0.84}{5.0} = 0.17$$

$$[PCl_3] = \frac{1.16}{5.0} = 0.23$$

$$[Cl_2] = \frac{0.16}{5.0} = 0.032$$

35 | 0.84

1.16

0.16

4 A 1.00-mole sample of PCl_5 was introduced into a container as indicated at the right. If there is now only 0.75 mole of PCl_5, there must be . . . . . . mole(s) of PCl_3 and . . . . . . mole(s) of Cl_2.

15 A reaction cell (right) is found to contain, after heating at a high temperature, 0.12 mole of H_2O. Fill in the following table:

	Initially	Used up	Remaining
Moles H_2	0.52		
Moles O_2	0.26		

26 In one experiment the equilibrium concentrations of the reagents at 250°C were found to be those shown at right. Calculate the value of K at this temperature: K = ...

37 To begin the calculation of the amounts of reagents present in the system at right, write concentration expressions with x as the number of moles of N_2O_4 that have dissociated.

$$N_2O_4(g) \rightleftharpoons 2NO_2(g)$$

initial moles	___	___
equil. moles	___	___
equil. conc.	___	___

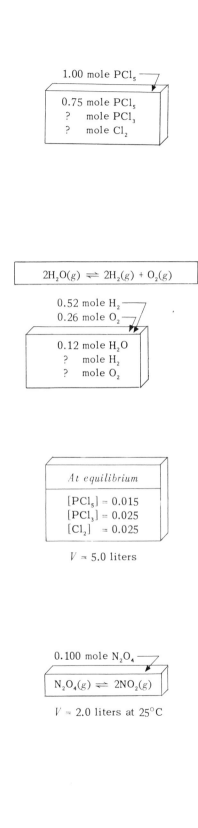

3 | de

in

14 | $2y$

$n - 2y$

25 | $\dfrac{[PCl_3][Cl_2]}{[PCl_5]}$

36 | $K = \dfrac{(0.23)(0.032)}{0.17} = 0.043$

(0.042 is not obtained because the value of x was rounded off to two significant figures for item 35)

5| If 1.00 mole of PCl_5 had been introduced and x moles now remain, the amount of PCl_3 present would be . . . . moles.

16| In order to perform calculations like those in the preceding items, the . . . . for the reaction must be known.

27| If the cell had originally been filled with pure PCl_5, its concentration before dissociation must have been . . . . , and there must have been . . . . mole of it.

38| Write the equilibrium expression and, using the given value of K, develop an expression from which x can be calculated.

ANSWERS

1.00 mole PCl_5

x mole PCl_5
? mole PCl_3

4 | 0.25

0.25

15 |

Used up	Remaining
0.12	0.40
0.06	0.20

At equilibrium

$[PCl_5] = 0.015$
$[PCl_3] = 0.025$
$[Cl_2] = 0.025$

$V = 5.0$ liters

26 | $$\frac{(0.025)(0.025)}{0.015} = 0.042$$

$N_2O_4(g) \rightleftharpoons 2NO_2(g)$
K = 0.0058 at 25° C

37 |

initial moles	0.100	0
equil. moles	$0.100 - x$	$2x$
equil. conc., (moles/liter)	$\frac{0.100 - x}{2.0}$	$\frac{2x}{2.0}$

6| A 1.00-mole sample of PCl_5 is introduced into a 5.0-liter vessel. The *initial* (before any dissociation) *concentration* is . . . . mole/liter. The concentration of PCl_5 will . . . . .crease with time.

17| It is sometimes convenient to write the initial and later amounts beneath the symbols in an equation as at the right. Complete the entries.

28| In another experiment, 1.8 moles of PCl_5 is added to the reaction chamber and allowed to come to equilibrium. Complete the entries at the right in terms of the unknown x, the number of moles of PCl_5 that dissociate.

39| Solution of the quadratic gives $x = 0.016$. Tabulate the number of moles and the concentrations at equilibrium:

	N_2O_4	NO_2
moles	_____	_____
conc.	_____	_____

5 | $1.00 - x$

16 | equation

PCl$_5$ (g) ⇌ PCl$_3$(g) + Cl$_2$(g)		
Initial moles	0.83	0.19	0
Later moles	0.71		

PCl$_5$(g) ⇌ PCl$_3$(g) + Cl$_2$(g)		
Initial moles	1.8	0	0
Equil. moles	1.8 − x		
Equil. conc., moles/ liter			

V = 5.0 liters

27 | 0.040 mole/liter

(0.040)(5.0) = 0.20

N$_2$O$_4$(g) ⇌ 2NO$_2$(g)	
Moles	0.100 − x	2x
Conc., moles/liter	$\dfrac{0.100 - x}{2.0}$	$\dfrac{2x}{2.0}$

V = 2.0 liters

38 |

$$0.0058 = \frac{[NO_2]^2}{[N_2O_4]} = \frac{(2x/2.0)^2}{(0.100 - x)/2.0}$$

$$= \frac{2.0x^2}{0.100 - x}$$

7| A 10.0-liter container, as at the right, into which 1.00 mole of
PCl_5 had been introduced, contains . . . . . . mole(s) of PCl_3. The
concentration of PCl_3 is . . . . mole(s) per liter.

18| Complete the entries at right.

29| The second step in the calculation of amounts at equilibrium is the
substitution of concentration expressions and the value of K, as
at the right, to obtain the expression . . . . $=$ . . . .,
from which x can be calculated.

40| The per cent of N_2O_4 that dissociates (in the system treated in the
preceding items) is . . . .

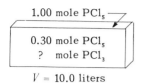

1.00 mole PCl₅

0.30 mole PCl₅
?   mole PCl₃

$V = 10.0$ liters

6 | 0.20

de

$2H_2O(g) \rightleftharpoons 2H_2(g) + O_2(g)$		
Initial moles	5.8	0	0
Later moles	2.0		

17 | $PCl_3(g) + Cl_2(g)$
        0.19   0
       +0.12   +0.12
       = 0.31   = 0.12

$PCl_5(g) \rightleftharpoons PCl_3(g) + Cl_2(g)$		
Equil. conc.	$\dfrac{1.8 - x}{5.0}$	$\dfrac{x}{5.0}$	$\dfrac{x}{5.0}$

K = 0.042 at 250° C

28 |

$PCl_5(g) \rightleftharpoons PCl_3(g) + Cl_2(g)$		
1.8	0	0
$1.8 - x$	x	x
$\dfrac{1.8 - x}{5.0}$	$\dfrac{x}{5.0}$	$\dfrac{x}{5.0}$

	At equilibrium	
	$N_2O_4(g) \rightleftharpoons 2NO_2(g)$	
Moles	0.084	0.032
Conc., moles/liter	0.042	0.016

39 | N_2O_4 NO_2

N_2O_4	NO_2
0.084	0.032
0.042	0.016

8 | A container of volume V originally contained only n moles of PCl_5.

If x moles of PCl_3 are formed, there remain . . . . . . mole(s) of PCl_5. The concentrations are then:

$$PCl_5 = \text{. . . . . . .} \text{ moles/liter}$$
$$PCl_3 = \text{. . . . . . .} \text{ moles/liter}$$
$$Cl_2 \ = \text{. . . . . . .} \text{ moles/liter}$$

19 | Complete the entries at the right.

30 | Solution of the quadratic equation (verify if you like) gives $x = 0.52$. Thus the equilibrium amounts are:

$$PCl_5 = \text{. . . . . . .} \text{ mole(s)}$$
$$PCl_3 = \text{. . . . . . .} \text{ mole(s)}$$
$$Cl_2 \ = \text{. . . . . . .} \text{ mole(s)}$$

41 | Calculations can be made directly in terms of concentrations (i.e., moles per liter). Let x = moles per liter of N_2O_4 that dissociate. Tabulate the equilibrium concentrations:

$$N_2O_4(g) \rightleftharpoons 2NO_2(g)$$

initially $[N_2O_4]$ = ... $[NO_2]$ = ...

at equil. $[N_2O_4]$ = ... $[NO_2]$ = ...

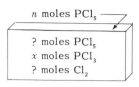

n moles PCl_5

? moles PCl_5
x moles PCl_3
? moles Cl_2

volume = V liters

7 | 0.70

0.070

$2CO_2(g) \rightleftharpoons 2CO(g) + O_2(g)$		
Initial moles	0.0	0.8	0.8
Later moles	0.2		

18 | $2H_2(g) + O_2(g)$

$5.8 - 2.0 \quad \frac{1}{2}(3.8)$

$= 3.8 \qquad = 1.9$

$PCl_5(g) \rightleftharpoons PCl_3(g) + Cl_2(g)$		
Equil. moles	$1.8 - x$	x	x

$$\frac{x^2}{5.0(1.8 - x)} = 0.042$$

29 |

$$0.042 = \frac{(x/5.0)(x/5.0)}{(1.8 - x)/5.0}$$

$$= \frac{x^2}{5.0(1.8 - x)}$$

2.0 moles N_2O_4

$N_2O_4(g) \rightleftharpoons 2NO_2(g)$

V = 12.6 liters

40 | $(0.016/0.100)(100) = 16\%$

9| The concentration in moles per liter is often indicated by placing brackets about its formula. Thus $[PCl_5] = 0.20$ means that the concentration of PCl_5 is . . . .

20| The *concentrations* of the reagents in a reacting system can be calculated if one knows the number of . . . . . . of the reagents and the . . . . . . of the system.

31| The per cent of dissociation is sometimes given. In the example of the previous item, ... mole(s) of the original 1.8 moles dissociated; we calculate % dissociation = .../1.8×100 = ...%.

42| An expression that permits the calculation of the number of . . . . per . . . . of N_2O_4 that dissociate is . . . . $\doteq$ . . . .

8 | $n - x$

$$\dfrac{n - x}{V} \quad \dfrac{x}{V} \quad \dfrac{x}{V}$$

19 | $2CO(g) + O_2(g)$

$0.8 - 0.2 \quad 0.8 - 0.1$

$= 0.6 \qquad = 0.7$

At equilibrium

PCl_5 = 1.3 moles
PCl_3 = 0.52 mole
Cl_2 = 0.52 mole

30 | 1.3

0.52

0.52

$N_2O_4(g) \rightleftharpoons 2NO_2(g)$	
Equil. conc.	$0.16 - x$ $2x$ moles/liter
	$K = 0.0058$ at 25° C

41 | $2.0/12.6 = 0.16 \qquad 0$

$0.16 - x \qquad\qquad 2x$

10| In the system at the right, which resulted from the addition of PCl_5
to the reaction chamber, $[PCl_5]$ = ...; $[PCl_3]$ = ...;
and $[Cl_2]$ = ...

21| Complete the entries for hydrogen, nitrogen, and ammonia at the
right.

32| In the system at the right, let x be the number of moles of PCl_5 that
dissociate. Write expressions for the number of moles of the reagents:

$$PCl_5(g) \rightleftharpoons PCl_3(g) + Cl_2(g)$$

moles   _____   _____   _____

43| Solution of this equation gives x = 0.015 mole/liter, and the equi-
librium concentrations are $[N_2O_4]$ = ... and $[NO_2]$ =
. . . .

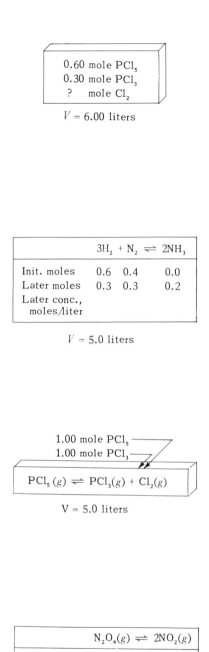

0.60 mole PCl_5
0.30 mole PCl_3
? mole Cl_2

$V = 6.00$ liters

9 | 0.20 mole/liter

	$3H_2$	$+ N_2$	$\rightleftharpoons 2NH_3$
Init. moles	0.6	0.4	0.0
Later moles	0.3	0.3	0.2
Later conc., moles/liter			

$V = 5.0$ liters

20 | moles

volume

1.00 mole PCl_5
1.00 mole PCl_3

$PCl_5(g) \rightleftharpoons PCl_3(g) + Cl_2(g)$

$V = 5.0$ liters

31 | 0.52

$(0.52/1.8)(100) = 29\%$

$N_2O_4(g) \rightleftharpoons 2NO_2(g)$	
Equil. conc. $0.16 - x$	$2x$

42 | moles

liter

$$0.0058 = \frac{(2x)^2}{0.16 - x}$$

11| If PCl_5 is introduced into a container at $250°C$, some PCl_3 and some Cl_2 will form. The dissociation equation . . . .

shows that the amounts of PCl_3 and Cl_2 will be . . . .

(*return to page* 95)

22| Complete the table at right.

(*return to page* 95)

33| Write expressions for the concentrations of the reagents in the system at right.

$$PCl_5(g) \rightleftharpoons PCl_3(g) + Cl_2(g)$$

Conc. moles/liter   _____   _____   _____

(*return to page* 95)

44| Let x represent the number of moles of hydrogen iodide (HI) that dissociate to obtain equilibrium. Develop the expression that permits the calculation of x (and therefore of the amounts at equilibrium).

(*turn to page* 106)

10 | 0.60/6.00 = 0.10

0.30/6.00 = 0.050

0.30/6.00 = 0.050

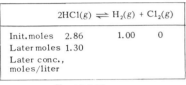

$V = 12.9$ liters

21 | 0.06 (H_2)

0.06 (N_2)

0.04 (NH_3)

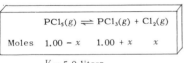

$V = 5.0$ liters

32 | $PCl_5(g) \rightleftharpoons PCl_3(g) + Cl_2(g)$

$1.00 - x \quad 1.00 + x \quad x$

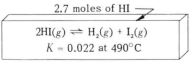

$V = 4.3$ liters

43 | 0.16 − 0.015 = 0.14

(2)(0.015) = 0.030

44|

$$2HI(g) \rightleftharpoons H_2(g) + I_2(g)$$

init. moles	2.7	0	0
equil. moles	$2.7 - x$	$x/2$	$x/2$

equil. conc. $\left[\dfrac{2.7 - x}{4.3}\right]$ $\left[\dfrac{x}{2(4.3)}\right]$ $\left[\dfrac{x}{2(4.3)}\right]$

$K = \dfrac{[H_2][I_2]}{[HI]^2}$ $0.022 = \dfrac{(x/8.6)(x/8.6)}{[(2.7 - x)/4.3]^2} = \dfrac{x^2}{4.0(2.7 - x)^2}$

$x = 0.62$ mole

moles of H_2 and of I_2 at equilibrium $= 0.31$

moles of HI at equilibrium $= 2.1$

or

$$2HI(g) \rightleftharpoons H_2(g) + I_2(g)$$

init. conc.	$\dfrac{2.7}{4.3} = 0.63$	0	0
equil. conc.	$0.63 - y$	$y/2$	$y/2$

where y = no. of moles/liter of HI that dissociate

$0.022 = \dfrac{(y/2)(y/2)}{(0.63 - y)^2} = \dfrac{y^2}{4(0.63 - y)^2}$

$y = 0.14$ mole/liter

$[H_2] = [I_2] = 0.07$ mole/liter

$[HI] = 0.49$ mole/liter

(turn to page 107)

A NOTHER type of equilibrium problem frequently encountered involves aqueous solutions. We shall look at two types; the first is equilibria that are established when ionic materials partially dissolve in water. In a saturated solution of $PbSO_4$, for example, an equilibrium exists between solid $PbSO_4$ and the Pb^{++} ions and $SO_4^=$ ions in solution.

$$PbSO_4(s) \rightleftharpoons Pb^{++} + SO_4^=$$

The equilibrium constant, written according to the rules with which you should be familiar (in particular, the fact that pure solid phases are omitted from the expression), is

$$K = [Pb^{++}] [SO_4^=]$$

Such equilibrium expressions are usually referred to as solubility products (generally indicated by K_{sp}). The solubility products of ionic compounds will be used here to obtain the concentration of ions in a saturated solution.

An example of the second type of equilibrium in solution, to be discussed here, is the partial dissociation of nitrous acid:

$$HNO_2 \rightleftharpoons H^+ + NO_2^-$$

The equilibrium constant (often called the acidity constant K_a) for this example is

$$K_a = \frac{[H^+] [NO_2^-]}{[HNO_2]}$$

(More correctly, as discussed in the chapter on acids and bases, one should write the dissociation equation $HNO_2 + H_2O \rightleftharpoons H_3O^+ + NO_2^-$. However, since the concentration of water remains essentially unchanged, its value can be included in the acidity constant itself. This would then be written

$$K_a = \frac{[H_3O^+] [NO_2^-]}{[HNO_2]}$$

This expression is identical in form to the abbreviated expression containing H^+ in place of H_3O^+.)

THE types of problems to be discussed in this section are illustrated by the following examples.

What is the solubility at 20°C of calcium fluoride (CaF_2) in an aqueous solution containing 0.010 M NaF? The solubility product of CaF_2 at 20°C is 1.7×10^{-10}.

What is the percent dissociation of 0.0050 M HNO_2 in aqueous solution if K_a for HNO_2 is 4.5×10^{-4}?

45 | The solubility of silver chloride in water is 1.27×10^{-5} mole/liter at 25°C. That is, a liter of saturated solution contains . . . . mole of AgCl.

58 | The solubility product for CaF_2 is 1.7×10^{-10} at 20°C. Substitution of this and the concentration expressions into the equilibrium expression gives the equation . . . .

71 | Solution of the equation of the preceding item gives $x = 1.7 \times 10^{-6}$. Therefore $[Ca^{++}] = $ . . . . and $[F^-] = $ . . . .

84 | Let $x = [H^+] = [NO_2^-]$ at equilibrium. Write the concentration expressions for a 0.0200-M HNO_2 solution:

$$HNO_2 \rightleftharpoons H^+ + NO_2^-$$

equil. conc.　　　＿＿＿　＿＿＿　＿＿＿

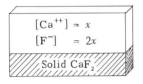

57 | x

$2x$

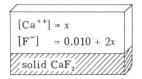

70 | $K_{sp} = [Ca^{++}][F^-]^2$

$1.7 \times 10^{-10} = (x)(0.010 + 2x)^2$

83 | 0.0013

$0.0013/0.100 = 0.013$ or 1.3%

46| If the dissolved AgCl is completely dissociated into Ag^+ and Cl^- ions, there is . . . . mole of Ag^+ in a liter of saturated solution; i.e., $[Ag^+]$ = ...

59| Solution of the equation of the preceding item gives x = 3.5×10^{-4}. Thus, in a saturated CaF_2 solution at 20°C, $[Ca^{++}]$ = ... and $[F^-]$ = ...

72| Solubilities can be calculated from solubility products. As in gas-phase-equilibrium calculations, the first step involves expressing the . . . . of the ions, as has been done with the symbol x.

85| Using K_a = 4.5×10^{-4} at 25°C, derive an algebraic expression from which the value of x can be calculated: . . . .

45 1.27×10^{-5}

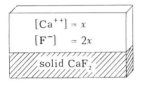

58 $x(2x)^2 = 4x^3 = 1.7 \times 10^{-10}$

71 1.7×10^{-6}

0.010

84 $HNO_2 \rightleftharpoons H^+ + NO_2^-$

$0.0200 - x \quad x \quad x$

47 What is [Cl⁻] in the saturated solution at the right?. . . . .

60 From the result of the preceding item, the solubility of CaF_2 can be calculated from its solubility product. This solubility is found to be . . . .

73 In the second step, these concentration expressions and the value of the . . . . are inserted into expressions like those at the right, which have already been studied.

86 Solution of the quadratic equation gives $x = 0.0028$, and therefore $[H^+] = $ . . . .; $[NO_2^-] = $ . . . .; and $[HNO_2] = $ . . . .

46 1.27×10^{-5}

1.27×10^{-5}

59 3.5×10^{-4}

7.0×10^{-4}

72 concentrations

85 $K_a = \dfrac{[H^+][NO_2^-]}{[HNO_2]}$

$4.5 \times 10^{-4} = \dfrac{x^2}{(0.0200 - x)}$

48 The saturated solution at the right is at equilibrium; hence we can calculate $K_{sp} = [Ag^+][Cl^-]$ to be . . . .

61 AgCl is dissolved in a $0.010-M$ NaCl solution. Before any AgCl dissolves, $[Cl^-]$ = ...

74 Finally, the algebraic equation is solved for x. From this, the desired . . . . of the salt in moles per liter can be obtained.

87 The degree of dissociation of $0.0200\ M$ HNO_2 at $25°C$ can be calculated from the results of the preceding item to be . . . . or . . . . %.

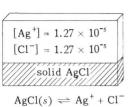

$[Ag^+] = 1.27 \times 10^{-5}$
$[Cl^-] = 1.27 \times 10^{-5}$
solid AgCl

$AgCl(s) \rightleftharpoons Ag^+ + Cl^-$

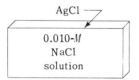

AgCl

0.010-M
NaCl
solution

<u>ANSWERS</u>

47| 1.27×10^{-5}

60| 3.5×10^{-4} mole/liter

73| solubility product (or equilibrium
constant)

86| 0.0028
   0.0028
   0.0172

49 When silver bromide dissolves in water, each mole that dissolves produces . . . . . mole of Ag^+ and . . . . . mole of Br^-.

62 When the solution is saturated with AgCl, $[Ag^+] = x$. The $[Cl^-]$ resulting from the dissolved AgCl is . . . . ., but the *total* $[Cl^-]$ = ...

75 In a solution made by adding water to 1.00 mole of nitrous acid (HNO_2) to make a liter of solution, ionization will occur as indicated. Complete the entries at the right.

88 Repeat the procedure of the preceding items to obtain a value for the per cent dissociation of HNO_2 in a 0.100-M solution. For $ax^2 + bx + c = 0$, $x = \dfrac{-b \pm \sqrt{b^2 - 4ac}}{2a}$.

$AgBr(s) \rightleftharpoons Ag^+ + Br^-$
in solution

48 | $(1.27 \times 10^{-5})(1.27 \times 10^{-5}) =$
1.61×10^{-10}

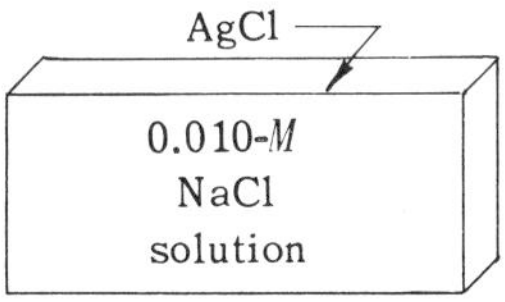

AgCl
0.010-M
NaCl
solution

61 | 0.010

$HNO_2 \rightleftharpoons H^+ + NO_2^-$
Equil. conc. _____ x _____

74 | solubility (or concentration)

$HNO_2 \rightleftharpoons H^+ + NO_2^-$
$K_a = 4.5 \times 10^{-4}$

87 | 0.0028/0.0200 = 0.14 or 14%

50| If $[Ag^+]$ in the saturated solution is x, in this solution $[Br^-] = \cdot \ldots$

63| Substitution of the concentration expressions and the value 1.6×10^{-10} for K_{sp} for AgCl at 25°C gives the equation . . . .

76| The expression for the acidity constant of HNO_2 has the form $K_a =$ . . . . If $K_a = 4.5 \times 10^{-4}$ at 25°C, the value of x can be calculated from the equation . . . .

89| From the results of preceding calculations (right), note that, as the concentration is lowered, the degree of dissociation . . . . . creases.

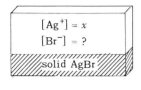

$[Ag^+] = x$
$[Br^-] = ?$
solid AgBr

$[Ag^+] = x$
$[Cl^-] = 0.010 + x$
solid AgCl

$HNO_2 \rightleftharpoons H^+ + NO_2^-$
$K_a = 4.5 \times 10^{-4}$
at 0.10 M, 6.5% dissociation
at 0.020 M, 14% dissociation

49| 1

1

62| x

$0.010 + x$

75| $HNO_2 \rightleftharpoons H^+ + NO_2^-$

$1.00 - x \quad x \qquad x$

88| $HNO_2 \rightleftharpoons H^+ + NO_2^-$
$0.100 - x \quad x \qquad x$

$4.5 \times 10^{-4} = x^2/(0.100 - x)$
$x = 0.0065$

$[H^+] = 0.0065 \quad [NO_2^-] = 0.0065$

per cent dissociation =
$(0.0065/0.100)(100) = 6.5\%$

51| Substituting x and the value of 7.7×10^{-13} (for K_{sp}) in the solubility-constant expression gives the equation . . . .; therefore $x =$ . . . .

64| Solution of the equation of the previous item gives $x = 1.6 \times 10^{-8}$; therefore $[Ag^+] =$ . . . . and $[Cl^-] =$ . . . .

77| Solution of this equation gives $x = 0.021$. The equilibrium concentrations are $[H^+] =$ . . . .; $[NO_2^-] =$ . . . .; and $[HNO_2] =$ . . . .

90| To calculate the per cent dissociation of HNO_2 in the system at right, first write the concentration expressions (using x) for $[HNO_2]$, $[H^+]$, and $[NO_2^-]$.

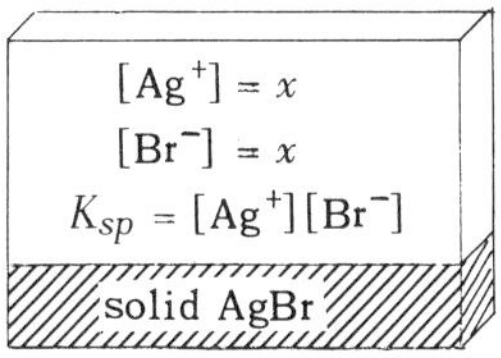

$$[Ag^+] = x$$
$$[Br^-] = x$$
$$K_{sp} = [Ag^+][Br^-]$$
solid AgBr

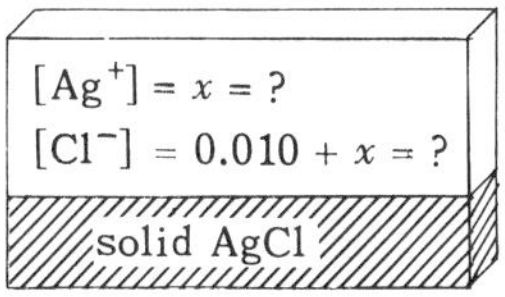

50 x

$$[Ag^+] = x = ?$$
$$[Cl^-] = 0.010 + x = ?$$
solid AgCl

63 $x(0.010 + x) = 1.6 \times 10^{-10}$

At equilibrium
$[H^+] = x$
$[NO_2^-] = x$
$[HNO_2] = 1.00 - x$

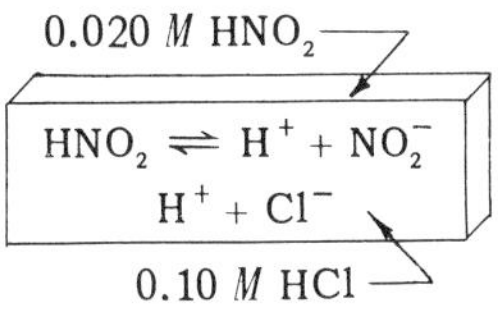

76 $\dfrac{[H^+][NO_2^-]}{[HNO_2]}$

$$4.5 \times 10^{-4} = \frac{x^2}{1.00 - x}$$

0.020 M HNO$_2$

$$HNO_2 \rightleftharpoons H^+ + NO_2^-$$
$$H^+ + Cl^-$$

0.10 M HCl

89 in

52| The result of the preceding item shows that the amount of AgBr

dissolved is . . . . mole/liter; in other words, the solu-

bility of AgBr is . . . . at 25°C.

65| What is the solubility of AgCl in a 0.010-M solution of NaCl?

. . . .

78| Acetic acid (CH$_3$COH) is a weak acid that dissociates according

to the equation CH$_3$COH $\rightleftharpoons$ H$^+$+ CH$_3$CO$^-$. The acidity-constant ex-

pression is K_a =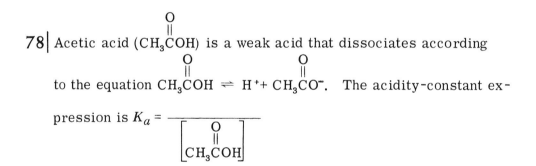

91| Write the algebraic expression for the calculation of the value of x.

51| $7.7 \times 10^{-13} = x^2$

$x = 8.8 \times 10^{-7}$ mole/liter

$[Ag^+] = 1.6 \times 10^{-8}$
$[Cl^-] = 0.010$
$[Na^+] = 0.010$
solid AgCl

64| 1.6×10^{-8}

0.010 (to two significant figures)

77| 0.021

0.021

0.98

$HNO_2 \rightleftharpoons H^+ + NO_2^-$
$0.020 - x \quad 0.10 + x \quad x$
$K_a = 4.5 \times 10^{-4}$

90| $HNO_2 \rightleftharpoons H^+ + NO_2^-$

$0.020 - x \quad 0.10 + x \quad x$

53 When lead chloride ($PbCl_2$) dissolves in water, each mole of $PbCl_2$ dissolved produces 1 mole of Pb^{++} and . . . . . mole(s) of Cl^-.

66 Calculate the solubility of AgCl ($K_{sp} = [Ag^+][Cl^-] = 1.6 \times 10^{-10}$) in pure water. . . . .

79 The dissociation of x moles of $CH_3\overset{O}{\overset{\|}{C}}OH$ will produce . . . . . moles of H^+ and . . . . . moles of $CH_3\overset{O}{\overset{\|}{C}}O$.

92 Solving the quadratic equation (item 91) gives $x = 9.0 \times 10^{-5}$. Tabulate the equilibrium concentrations: $[H^+] =$ . . . .; $[NO_2^-] =$ . . . .; and $[HNO_2] =$ . . . .

$$PbCl_2(s) \rightleftharpoons Pb^{++} + 2Cl^-$$

52 | 8.8×10^{-7}
8.8×10^{-7} mole/liter

65 | 1.6×10^{-8} mole/liter

$$CH_3\overset{\overset{\displaystyle O}{\|}}{C}OH \rightleftharpoons H^+ + CH_3\overset{\overset{\displaystyle O}{\|}}{C}O^-$$

78 | $\dfrac{[H^+][CH_3\overset{\overset{\displaystyle O}{\|}}{C}O^-]}{[CH_3\overset{\overset{\displaystyle O}{\|}}{C}OH]}$

$$HNO_2 \rightleftharpoons H^+ + NO_2^-$$
$$0.020 - x \quad 0.10 + x \quad x$$

91 | $K_a = \dfrac{[H^+][NO_2^-]}{[HNO_2]}$ and

$$4.5 \times 10^{-4} = \frac{(0.10 + x)(x)}{(0.020 - x)}$$

54 The solubility of $PbCl_2$ is 0.016 mole/liter at 20°C. In a saturated solution $[Pb^{++}]$ = ...; $[Cl^-]$ = ...

67 The results at the right show that the presence of one of the ions of the dissolving salt, a *common ion,* results in a(n). . . . . creased solubility.

80 If, in a 0.100-*M* solution of $CH_3\overset{\overset{O}{\|}}{C}OH$ no $CH_3\overset{\overset{O}{\|}}{C}OH$ dissociated, $[CH_3\overset{\overset{O}{\|}}{C}OH]$ would be 0.100. If x moles/liter dissociate, $[CH_3\overset{\overset{O}{\|}}{C}OH]$ = ...

93 What is the per cent dissociation of 0.020 *M* HNO_2 in a solution containing 0.10 *M* HCl? . . . .

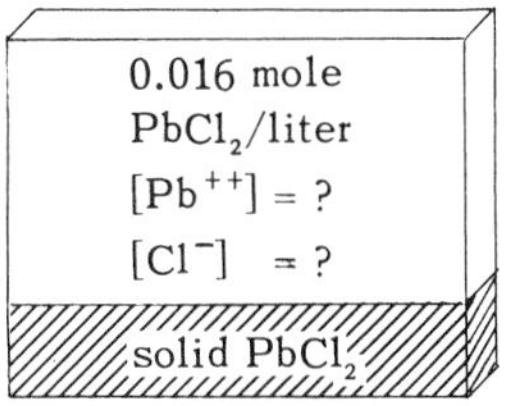
0.016 mole
PbCl2/liter
[Pb++] = ?
[Cl−] = ?
solid PbCl2

ANSWERS

53 | 2

$AgCl(s) \rightleftharpoons Ag^+ + Cl^-$
in 0.010 *M* NaCl, solubility of
AgCl = 1.6×10^{-8} mole/liter
in pure water, solubility of
AgCl = 1.3×10^{-5} mole/liter

66 | let $[Ag^+] = x$ $[Cl^-] = x$

then $K_{sp} = [Ag^+][Cl^-]$
or $1.6 \times 10^{-10} = x^2$
and $x = 1.3 \times 10^{-5}$

solubility = 1.3×10^{-5} mole/liter

79 | x

x

At equilibrium	
$[HNO_2]$	= 0.020
$[NO_2^-]$	= 9.0×10^{-5}
$[H^+]$	= 0.10
$[Cl^-]$	= 0.10

92 | 0.10

9.0×10^{-5}

0.020

55| The solubility product of $PbCl_2$ has the form $K_{sp} = [Pb^{++}][Cl^-]^2$.

The value of the constant can be calculated: K_{sp} = ...

$\doteq$ . . . .

68| When CaF_2 dissolves in $0.010\text{-}M$ NaF solution, x moles dissolve per liter. In this saturated solution $[Ca^{++}]$ = ...

81| If x represents the extent of dissociation required for a state of equilibrium (see right), the concentration expressions and the value

of K_a can be used to give the algebraic equation . . . .

94| Let x be the concentration of H^+ formed by the dissociation of HF in the system at right. Set up an algebraic equation that allows the value of x, and thus of the equilibrium concentrations, to be calculated.

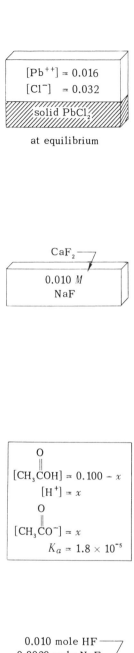

$[Pb^{++}] = 0.016$
$[Cl^-] = 0.032$
solid PbCl$_2$

at equilibrium

54 | 0.016

0.032

CaF$_2$

0.010 M
NaF

67 | de

$$[CH_3\overset{\overset{O}{\|}}{C}OH] = 0.100 - x$$
$$[H^+] = x$$
$$[CH_3\overset{\overset{O}{\|}}{C}O^-] = x$$
$$K_a = 1.8 \times 10^{-5}$$

80 | $0.100 - x$

0.010 mole HF
0.0020 mole NaF

$HF \rightleftharpoons H^+ + F^-$
$K_a = 6.7 \times 10^{-4}$

V = 1.0 liter

93 | $\dfrac{9.0 \times 10^{-5}}{0.020} \times 100 = 0.45\%$

56| The dissolution of 1 mole of CaF_2 produces . . . . . mole(s) of

Ca^{++} and . . . . . mole(s) of F^-.

69| The $[F^-]$ in this solution as a result of the NaF present is . . . . . . ,

and that from CaF_2 is . . . . The total $[F^-]$ is . . . .

82| Solution of this equation gives $x = 0.0013$; thus the equilibrium

concentrations are $[H^+]$ = ...; $\begin{bmatrix} O \\ \parallel \\ CH_3CO^- \end{bmatrix}$ = ...;

and $\begin{bmatrix} O \\ \parallel \\ CH_3COH \end{bmatrix}$ = ...

ANSWERS

$CaF_2(s) \rightleftharpoons Ca^{++} + 2F^-$

55 $K_{sp} = (0.016)(0.032)^2 = 1.6 \times 10^{-5}$

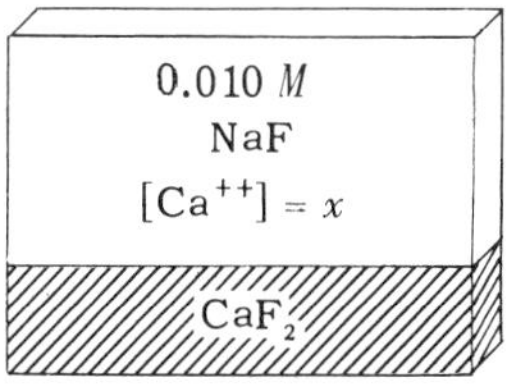
0.010 *M*
NaF
[Ca⁺⁺] = *x*
CaF₂

68 x

$[H^+] = x$

$[CH_3\overset{O}{\overset{\|}{C}}O^-] = x$

$[CH_3\overset{O}{\overset{\|}{C}}OH] = 0.100 - x$

81 $1.8 \times 10^{-5} = \dfrac{x^2}{0.100 - x}$

94

	HF	$\rightleftharpoons$	H^+	+	F^-
equil. conc.	$0.010 - x$		x		$0.0020 + x$

$K_a = \dfrac{[H^+][F^-]}{[HF]}$ or $6.7 \times 10^{-4} = \dfrac{x(0.0020 + x)}{0.010 - x}$

$x = 0.0016$

(*turn to page* 121)

57 | If x represents the number of moles of CaF_2 that are dissolved in a liter of solution, the concentrations are: $[Ca^{++}]$ = ... and $[F^-]$ = ...

(return to page 108)

70 | The solubility product for CaF_2 has the form . . . . and the value 1.7×10^{-10} at $20°C$. The expression that must be solved to obtain x is . . . .

(return to page 108)

83 | Of the 0.100 mole/liter of $CH_3\overset{\overset{\text{O}}{\|}}{C}OH$ introduced, ... mole(s)/liter dissociated. The fraction dissociated is . . . ./0.100 = ... , or . . . .%.

(return to page 108)

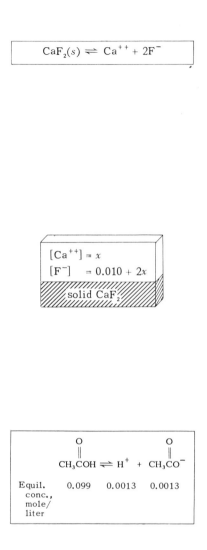

YOU now have learned how to do the basic problems that arise when equilibrium concentrations are to be obtained from given equilibrium constants. You have studied three particular types of chemical equilibria: homogeneous reactions in the gas state, the solution of slightly soluble salts in aqueous solution, and the dissociation of weak acids in aqueous solution, and have seen that the equilibrium calculations can be performed when a system is complicated by additional amounts of one of the species in equilibrium, as in the common-ion effect. The basic procedures for studying equilibria that you have learned from these systems will allow you to approach all types of equilibrium calculations.

CHAPTER SEVEN

Rates of

Chemical Reactions

MANY of the chemical reactions that are first encountered in the laboratory proceed from reactants to products so quickly that they appear to be instantaneous. Further study will show, however, that many reactions require an appreciable time to reach their final state. Study of the rates of such slow reactions is of obvious importance if one depends on the reactions for the products that are formed. Furthermore, study of the rates of reactions provides a remarkable insight into the way the reacting molecules, or ions, come together and rearrange to form the product molecules or ions.

The speed with which a reaction occurs depends on the concentration of the reactants and on the temperature of the system. In this chapter, only the effect of concentration will be considered.

The manner in which the rate of a reaction depends on the concentration of the reactants is quantitatively expressed by the *rate equation* for the reaction. In this section you will learn how to deduce the rate equation for a reaction from the observed effect of concentration on rate.

1| The general term *reagents* and the more specific terms *reactants* and *products* are often used in discussions of reaction rates. Insert these three terms in the appropriate places at right.

8| For any reaction A + B → products, the concentrations of A and B are represented, as usual, by [A] and [B] in moles per liter. The fact that the reaction rate is a function of the concentrations of the reactants can then be expressed in a general equation, by rate =

$f(\ldots \ldots \ldots, \ldots \ldots \ldots)$

15| A reaction that proceeds according to the rate equation rate = $k[A][B]^2$ can be said to be first order in A and second order in B. But the order of the over-all reaction corresponds to the sum of the exponents of [A] and [B] and is . . . .

22| The data at right refer to the reaction D + E → F. Compare entries 2 and 3. Doubling [D] (with [E] constant), ... the rate. Thus the rate is . . . . to [D].

7 | concentration (molarity)

14 | second-

$D + E \rightarrow F$			
	[D]	[E]	Rate*
1	0.37	1.26	0.036
2	0.37	0.63	0.009
3	0.74	0.63	0.018
*moles of F per liter per hour			

21 | rate = 0.0030 mole/liter-min

2| When we say that a chemical reaction occurs, we mean that re-
actants are, to some extent, transformed into . . . . in
some reasonable length of time.

9| If the rate of the reaction A + B → products is doubled when the
concentration of A is doubled, the rate must be directly propor-

tional to . . . .

16| The data at right were obtained for the reaction A + B → C. Entries

1 and 2 show that doubling [A], while holding [B] constant, ...
the rate.

23| Compare entries 1 and 2. Halving [E] (with [D] constant) decreases

the rate by a factor of . . . . . .

ANSWERS

1| reactants → products

reagents

8| [A], [B]

$A + B \rightarrow C$		
[A]	[B]	Rate*
1 1.0	1.0	0.15
2 2.0	1.0	0.30
3 3.0	1.0	0.45
4 1.0	2.0	0.15
5 1.0	3.0	0.15

*moles of product per liter
per minute

15| third

$D + E \rightarrow F$		
[D]	[E]	Rate*
1 0.37	1.26	0.036
2 0.37	0.63	0.009
3 0.74	0.63	0.018

*moles of F per liter per hour

22| doubles

proportional

3| When aqueous HCl and AgNO$_3$ solutions are mixed, the product of the reaction forms so rapidly that the reaction cannot be easily followed as a function of . . . .

10| If, moreover, in the same reaction the rate is found not to depend on the concentration of B, we can write a simple equation using the proportionality constant k: rate = ...

17| Since doubling [A] (holding [B] constant) doubles the rate, the rate is proportional to . . . .

24| Since halving [E] changes the rate by a factor of 4, the rate is not proportional to [E] but to . . . .

ANSWERS

$Ag^+ + Cl^- \rightarrow AgCl$

2 | products

$A + B \rightarrow$ products

9 | the concentration of A (or [A])

$A + B \rightarrow C$			
	[A]	[B]	Rate*
1	1.0	1.0	0.15
2	2.0	1.0	0.30
3	3.0	1.0	0.45
4	1.0	2.0	0.15
5	1.0	3.0	0.15

*moles of product per liter per minute

16 | doubles

$D + E \rightarrow F$			
	[D]	[E]	Rate*
1	0.37	1.26	0.036
2	0.37	0.63	0.009
3	0.74	0.63	0.018

*moles of F per liter per hour

23 | 4

4 | Other reactions, such as the hydrolysis reaction at the right, take hours to reach their final state, and the extent of reaction that has occurred during various intervals of . . . . can be determined.

11 | If doubling the concentration of a reagent increases the rate by a factor of 4, and tripling the concentration of the reagent increases the rate by a factor of 9, the rate is proportional to the . . . . of the concentration of the reagent.

18 | Entries 4 and 5, in the table on the right, show that changing [B] while holding [A] constant . . (does, does not) . . affect the rate.

25 | The rate is proportional to [D] and to [E]². The rate equation for the reaction is rate = ... The over-all order of the reaction is . . . ., or, as we sometimes say, ... order in D and . . . . order in E.

$$CH_3COC_2H_5 + H_2O \rightarrow$$

with O double-bonded above the C:

$$
\begin{array}{c}
\overset{\text{O}}{\underset{\|}{}} \\
CH_3COC_2H_5 + H_2O \rightarrow \\
\overset{\text{O}}{\underset{\|}{}} \\
CH_3COH + C_2H_5OH
\end{array}
$$

3 | time

10 | $k[A]$

$A + B \rightarrow C$		
	[A]	[B]	Rate*
1	1.0	1.0	0.15
2	2.0	1.0	0.30
3	3.0	1.0	0.45
4	1.0	2.0	0.15
5	1.0	3.0	0.15

*moles of product per liter per minute

17 | $[A]$

$D + E \rightarrow F$		
	[D]	[E]	Rate*
1	0.37	1.26	0.036
2	0.37	0.63	0.009
3	0.74	0.63	0.018

*moles of F per liter per hour

24 | $[E]^2$

5| Reactions generally proceed more rapidly as the concentrations of some of the reactants are increased. We say that the rate of the reaction is a function of the . . . . of the reactants.

12| If the rate of a reaction is proportional to the square of the concentration of A and independent of the concentrations of other reagents, the rate equation would have the form rate = k. . . . .

19| The rate equation for this reaction is, therefore, ...

26| Rate = $k[D][E]^2$: Using data from entry 1, evaluate k.

. . . .

$A + B \rightarrow C$			
	[A]	[B]	Rate*
1	1.0	1.0	0.15
2	2.0	1.0	0.30
3	3.0	1.0	0.45
4	1.0	2.0	0.15
5	1.0	3.0	0.15
*moles of product per liter per minute			

$D + E \rightarrow F$			
	[D]	[E]	Rate*
1	0.37	1.26	0.036
2	0.37	0.63	0.009
3	0.74	0.63	0.018
*moles of F per liter per hour			

6| By the *rate* of a reaction is meant the decrease in the amount of reactants, or the increase in the amount of . . . ., per unit interval of . . . .

13| If the rate of the reaction at the right is directly proportional to both [A] and [B], the equation defining the rate would take the form rate = k[A][B]. If the rate is proportional to [A] and to [B]^2, the rate equation would take the form . . . .

20| For this reaction, rate = k[A] or k = ... Use the data in entry 3 to determine the value and units of k. (Note that moles of product per liter per minute is also expressed as moles/liter-min.)

27| For the reaction of the preceding items you deduced that, at the temperature of the experiments, rate = 0.061[D][E]^2. Calculate the rate with which D would be used up in a solution with [D] = 1.0 and [E] = 0.020.

$A + B \rightarrow \text{products}$

$A + B \rightarrow C$			
	[A]	[B]	Rate*
1	1.0	1.0	0.15
2	2.0	1.0	0.30
3	3.0	1.0	0.45
4	1.0	2.0	0.15
5	1.0	3.0	0.15

*moles of product per liter per minute

$D + E \rightarrow F$

ANSWERS

5 | concentration

12 | $[A]^2$

19 | rate = $k[A]$

26 | $k = \dfrac{\text{rate}}{[D][E]^2} = \dfrac{0.036}{(0.37)(1.26)^2}$

$= 0.061(\text{moles/liter})^{-2}\,\text{hr}^{-1}$

7 | For reactions occurring in solution, the rate can be measured in terms of the change in the amount of reagent in a given volume of solution; i.e., the change in the . . . . of the reactants or products.

(*return to page* 123)

14 | The term *order of reaction* expresses the sum of the exponents to which the concentrations of the reagents are raised in the rate equation. Thus rate = $k[A]$ represents a first-order reaction,

whereas rate = $k[A]^2$ and rate = $k[A][B]$ both indicate . . . . order reactions.

(*return to page* 123)

21 | Given the value of k, it is a simple matter to calculate the rate at any concentration of A. What is the rate of the reaction when

$[A] = 0.020$? . . . .

(*return to page* 123)

6 | products

time

A + B → products

13 | rate = $k[A][B]^2$

A + B → C

rate = 0.15 [A]

20 | $\dfrac{\text{rate}}{[A]}$

$k = \dfrac{0.45 \text{ mole/liter-min}}{3.0 \text{ moles/liter}}$

$= 0.15 \text{ min}^{-1}$

27 | rate = $0.061(1.0)(0.020)^2$

$= 2.4 \times 10^{-5}$ moles/liter/hr

(rate of using up D equals rate of

formation of F)

(turn to page 130)

IN the preceding section you deduced the order of a reaction by finding the relation between the rate of reaction and the concentration of reactants. Nothing was said, however, about how the rate might have been measured. Experimentally, rates are not usually determined directly but are deduced from the way in which the concentrations of reactants vary with time. As an example, consider the decomposition of N_2O_5 in carbon tetrachloride (CCl_4). The reaction is $N_2O_5 \rightarrow N_2O_4 + \frac{1}{2}O_2$. The N_2O_4 formed is soluble in CCl_4, but the O_2 is not, and escapes from the solution as the reaction proceeds. By measuring the amount of O_2 evolved, one can calculate how much of the N_2O_5 has decomposed at any time and thus the concentration of N_2O_5 at any time. The following table shows data obtained for this reaction:

t, sec	$[N_2O_5]$
0	2.00
100	1.88
200	1.77
400	1.56
800	1.21
1200	0.955
1800	0.654
2400	0.450
3000	0.310

It is from such data that one must deduce the rate equation for the reaction.

    After finishing this section you will be able to perform such a calculation. The discussion will be limited to the simplest case, that of a first-order reaction. In this treatment, it should be mentioned, use will be made of calculus notation and you should, before working through the following material, be familiar with simple derivatives and integrations.

28| The $[N_2O_5]$ vs. time curve, plotted from the data on page 130, is shown at right. The tangent to this curve at t = 600 sec has the intercepts shown. Calculate the slope of the curve at t = 600 sec.

39| The rate of the N_2O_5 decomposition is equal to $-d[N_2O_5]/dt$. Since t was measured in seconds, the rate of the reaction has the units

of . . . .

50| Rearrangement of this relation between $[A]$ and t and replacement of natural logarithms by logs to the base 10, gives $\log [A] = -(k/2.303)t + \log [A]_0$. The slope of a plot of $\log [A]$ versus t

would be equal to . . . .

61| A relatively fast reaction is characterized by a . . . . rate

constant and a . . . . . . half-life.

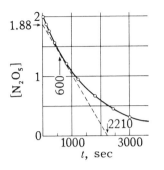

38 | 6.2×10^{-4}

49 | $C = -\ln [A]_0$

$-\ln [A] = kt - \ln[A]_0$

60 | $k = 0.693/23 = 0.030 \ \mathrm{min}^{-1}$

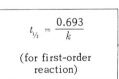

$t_{1/2} = \dfrac{0.693}{k}$

(for first-order reaction)

29| As the diagram at the right suggests, the slope of the curve at any point is related to the change in the concentration of N_2O_5 with time as slope = ...

40| What are the units of k for the N_2O_5 decomposition reaction?

. . . .

51| The equation of the previous item suggests a convenient graphical method for determining k for a first-order reaction. One would plot . . . . . vs. . . . . . . and, if the reaction were indeed first order, would obtain a straight line whose slope could be determined.

62| The rate constant for the N_2O_5 decomposition reaction was found in items 34 and 55 to be 6.2×10^{-4} mole/liter-sec. The time for one-half the N_2O_5 in a sample to be decomposed is calculated to be . . . .

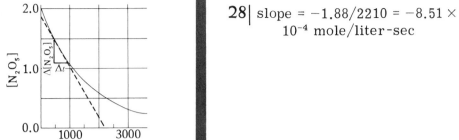

28| slope = $-1.88/2210 = -8.51 \times$ 10^{-4} mole/liter-sec

39| moles/liter-sec (i.e., mole liter^{-1} sec^{-1})

$$\log[A] = -\frac{k}{2.303}t + \log[A]_0$$

50| $-k/2.303$

$$t_{1/2} = \frac{0.693}{k}$$

(for first-order reaction)

61| large

short

30| With calculus notation this relation is expressed as slope =

. . . .

41| At what rate does N_2O_5 decompose in a solution when $[N_2O_5]$ =

0.600? . . . .

52| Deduce k from the data below:

t, sec	$[A]$	$log\,[A]$
0	1.0	0.000
100	0.80	−0.097
200	0.63	−0.201
300	0.50	−0.301
400	0.40	−0.398

63| Draw vertical dashed lines on the diagram to the right at the times
at which the N_2O_5 concentration decreases successively to one-
half its value, i.e., from 2.0 to 1.0, from 1.0 to 0.5, and so forth.

The half-life is seen to be . . . .

$29|$ $\dfrac{\Delta[N_2O_5]}{\Delta t}$

rate $= 6.2 \times 10^{-4}$ $[N_2O_5]$

$40|$ $k =$ rate$/[N_2O_5]$ and k has

units of $\dfrac{\text{moles/liter-sec}}{\text{moles/liter}}$

$= \text{sec}^{-1}$

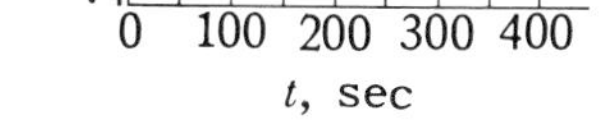

$51|$ $\log [A]$ vs. t

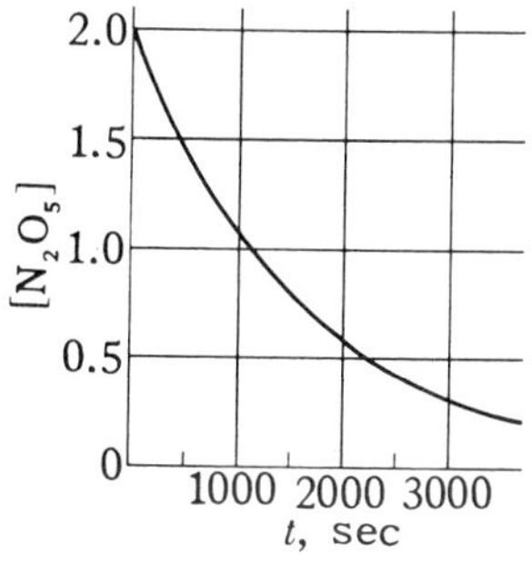

$62|$ $t_{\frac{1}{2}} = \dfrac{0.693}{6.2 \times 10^{-4}} = 1100$ sec

31| The slope of the curve, expressed by $d[N_2O_5]/dt$, shows the increase in $[N_2O_5]$ with time. The rate of reaction, however, is defined as the rate at which a reactant is *used up*, i.e., the rate with which $[N_2O_5]$ decreases, not increases. Thus the rate is related

to the slope by rate = ...

42| For the reaction A → products, which proceeds as shown at the right, complete the table.

t, sec	$[A]$	rate($= -$slope)
1000		
2000		
3000		
4000		

53| For a first-order reaction A → products, show the shape of the curve obtained when $[A]$ is plotted against t. The relation between $[A]$ and rate of the reaction is given by

the equation . . . .

64| The previous item shows graphically that the time for one-half of a reactant to be used up in a first-order reaction is independent of the concentration of the reactant. This is also shown by the absence of concentration in the $t_{\frac{1}{2}}$, k relation . . . .

30 $\left| \dfrac{d[N_2O_5]}{dt} \right.$

41 $\left|\; 3.7 \times 10^{-4} \text{ moles/liter-sec} \right.$

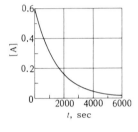

52 |

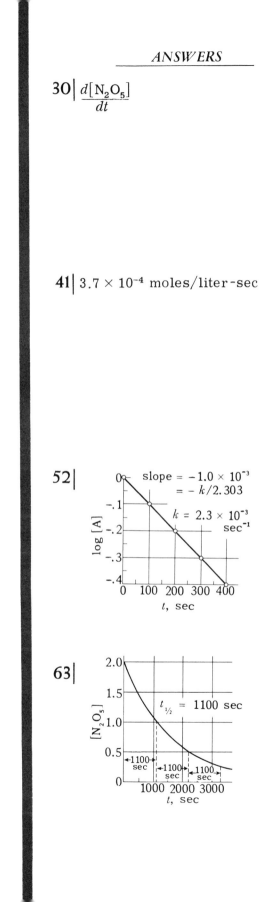

slope $= -1.0 \times 10^{-3}$
$= -k/2.303$

$k = 2.3 \times 10^{-3}$ sec^{-1}

63 |

$t_{1/2} = 1100$ sec

32| Thus we see that, if we plot the concentration of a reactant vs. time, the rate can be determined at any time as the . . . . of the slope of the curve.

43| Verify that the data of the previous item show that the rate equation for the reaction has the form rate = $k[A]$, and evaluate k.

54| For a first-order reaction, the relation between $\log [A]$ and t is $\log [A] = -(k/2.303)t + \log [A]_0$ and a plot of $\log [A]$ vs. t gives the curve

65| The rate of hydrolysis of methyl acetate ($CH_3\overset{\overset{O}{\|}}{C}OCH_3$) in a solu-
tion of given acidity depends only on the methyl acetate concen-
tration and is found to be a first-order reaction. The rate equa-

tion is rate = ..., or, in differential form, ...=

. . . .

ANSWERS

$31|$ $-\text{slope} = \dfrac{-d[N_2O_5]}{dt}$

$42|$

[A]	Rate, $\times 10^4$
0.31	2.0
0.16	1.0
0.083	0.55
0.043	0.28

$53|$

rate $= k[A]$

$64|$ $t_{\frac{1}{2}} = 0.693/k$

33| The slope of the curve at three distinct times is given at right. The rate of reaction . . . . . creases as the reaction proceeds.

44| The rate equation for the reaction of the preceding item, ..., shows that the reaction is . . . . order.

55| Determine the rate constant for the N_2O_5 decomposition by the method of plotting log $[N_2O_5]$ vs. t for the data below:

t, sec	$[N_2O_5]$	log $[N_2O_5]$
100	1.88	0.274
300	1.66	0.220
600	1.37	0.137
800	1.21	0.083

66| Plot the data given below and from the slope of the curve at 60 min deduce the rate constant for the reaction:

t, min	$[CH_3\overset{\text{O}}{\overset{\|}{C}}OCH_3]$
0	0.3
30	0.19
60	0.13
90	0.082
120	0.053
150	0.035

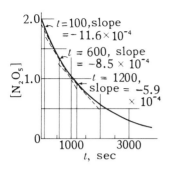

32 negative

43

t, sec	$k = \text{rate}/[A], \times 10^4$
1000	6.6
2000	6.6
3000	6.6
4000	6.6

54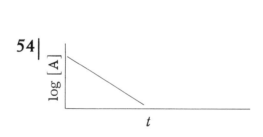

65 $k\left[\text{CH}_3\overset{\overset{\text{O}}{\|}}{\text{C}}\text{OCH}_3\right]$

$$-\frac{d\left[\text{CH}_3\overset{\overset{\text{O}}{\|}}{\text{C}}\text{OCH}_3\right]}{dt} = k\left[\text{CH}_3\overset{\overset{\text{O}}{\|}}{\text{C}}\text{OCH}_3\right]$$

34| The rate of reaction at three times is listed in the table at right. Complete the last column.

45| For any first-order reaction, where A → products, the rate at any time is . . . . to [A].

56| At the right are shown the differential and integral forms of the rate equation for a first-order reaction. Use the second of these to obtain an expression for the time at which a reaction is 90% complete, i.e., when $[A] = \frac{1}{10}[A]_o$. (Recall $\log x - \log y = \log x/y$.)

67| One could verify that the reaction is first order by determining the slope at various concentrations and seeing that all calculations, such as that of the previous item, give the same value of

. . . . . .

t, sec	$[N_2O_5]$	Rate, moles/ liter-sec	Rate/$[N_2O_5]$, sec^{-1}
100	1.88	11.6×10^{-4}	
600	1.37	8.5×10^{-4}	6.2×10^{-4}
1200	0.955	5.9×10^{-4}	

$$-\frac{d[A]}{dt} = k[A]$$

$$\log[A] = -\frac{k}{2.303}t + \log[A]_0$$

33 de

44 rate $= 6.6 \times 10^{-4}[A]$

first

55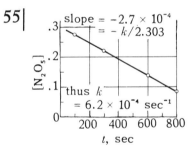

slope $= -2.7 \times 10^{-4}$
$= -k/2.303$

thus k
$= 6.2 \times 10^{-4}$ sec^{-1}

$[N_2O_5]$ vs t, sec

66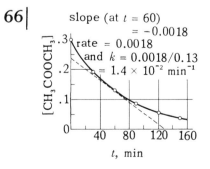

slope (at $t = 60$)
$= -0.0018$
rate $= 0.0018$
and $k = 0.0018/0.13$
$= 1.4 \times 10^{-2}$ min^{-1}

$[CH_3COOCH_3]$ vs t, min

35 | Although the rate is not constant, the quantity . . . .
does remain constant.

46 | Since the rate of an A → products type reaction can be expressed

by the derivative (note sign) . . . ., the rate equation, if
the reaction is first order, is the differential equation

. . . .

57 | The result of the previous item shows explicitly that, if k is large,

the time for 90% completion is correspondingly . . . .

68 | An alternative way of determining that the reaction is first order
is to mark off the half--lives. If the half–life is independent of
concentration the reaction is first order. Verify this on the figure at the right and use the value of $t_{\frac{1}{2}}$ to obtain another value for
k.

34 6.2×10^{-4}

6.2×10^{-4}

45 proportional

$\boxed{\begin{array}{l} t \text{ (for 90\% completion)} \\ \quad = \dfrac{2.303}{k} \end{array}}$

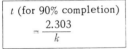

56 $\log [A] - \log [A]_o = -\dfrac{k}{2.303}\,t$

or $\log [A]/[A]_o = -(k/2.303)t$

Thus t for $[A] = \frac{1}{10}[A]_o$

is $-2.303/k \log \frac{1}{10} = 2.303/k$

67 k

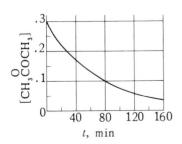

36| Since rate/$[N_2O_5]$ = k, you can write rate = k . . . ., i.e., the rate is . . . . to $[N_2O_5]$.

47| Such a differential equation can be converted to an integrated form that is often convenient for deducing rate equations from experimental data. First rearrange the equation so that $[A]$ and t appear on opposite sides of the equality. . . . .

58| The half-life of a reaction is the time required for the amount of A to drop to one-half the amount $[A]_0$ originally present. We denote this time as $t_{\frac{1}{2}}$ and see that, at this time, $[A]$ = ... $[A]_0$.

69| More representative of the way in which one obtains rate constants from concentration-time data is that in which a straight line plot is obtained and the rate constant is deduced from the slope of this curve. Use the following data to again obtain k for the methyl acetate hydrolysis:

t, min	$[CH_3\overset{O}{\overset{\|}{C}}OCH_3]$	$\log [CH_3\overset{O}{\overset{\|}{C}}OCH_3]$
0	0.30	−0.52
30	0.19	−0.72
60	0.13	−0.89
90	0.082	−1.09
120	0.053	−1.28
150	0.035	−1.46

35| rate/$[N_2O_5]$

46| $-\dfrac{d[A]}{dt}$

$-\dfrac{d[A]}{dt} = k[A]$

57| short

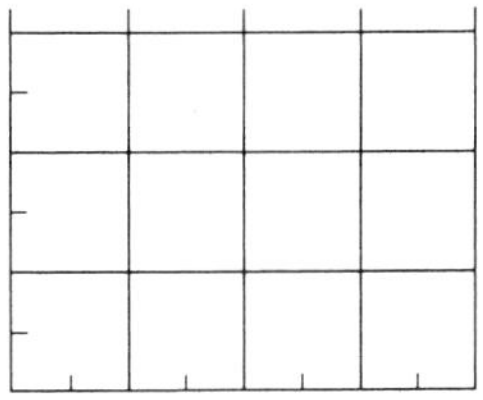

68| successive half lives are all equal. Their value is 50 min. Since $k = 0.693/t_{\frac{1}{2}}$, $k = 0.693/50$ $= 1.4 \times 10^{-2}$ min^{-1}

37 | The rate of this reaction at any time is given by rate = $k[N_2O_5]$.
This is a . . . .- order reaction.

48 | Integration of this equation yields $-\ln[A] = kt + C$ where C is a
constant of . . . .

59 | Obtain a compact expression for $t_{\frac{1}{2}}$ by substituting $[A] = \frac{1}{2}[A]_o$
and $t = t_{\frac{1}{2}}$ in the expression at the right, which shows the relation
between $[A]$ and t for a first-order reaction.

$$N_2O_5 \rightarrow N_2O_4 + \tfrac{1}{2} O_2$$

$$\log [A] = -\frac{k}{2.303} t + \log [A]_0$$

36 | $[N_2O_5]$
proportional

47 | $-\dfrac{d[A]}{[A]} = k\ dt$

58 | $\tfrac{1}{2}$

69 |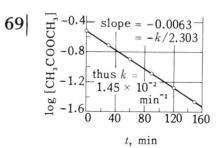

(*turn to page* 142)

38 Since the value of rate/$[N_2O_5]$ is 6.2×10^{-4}, k in the equation

rate $= k[N_2O_5]$ has the value . . . .

(*return to page* 131)

49 Since at $t = 0$, $[A] = [A]_0$ (the initial concentration of A), the con-

stant C can be evaluated as . . . ., and this used to re-

place C and give the equation . . . .

(*return to page* 131)

60 A certain first-order reaction is half completed in 23 minutes.

The rate constant for the reaction must be . . . .

(*return to page* 131)

37 | first

$$-\ln [A] = kt + C$$

48 | integration

$$t_{1/2} = \frac{0.693}{k}$$

(for first-order
reaction)

59 | $\log \frac{1}{2}[A]_0/[A]_0 = -kt_{\frac{1}{2}}/2.303$

$\log 2 = kt_{\frac{1}{2}}/2.303$

$t_{\frac{1}{2}} = 0.693/k$

NOW that you have studied some aspects of the rates with which chemical reactions proceed, or, as is often said, chemical kinetics, you see that the rate equation for a reaction and the rate constant that appears in this equation can be deduced from experimental results for the amount of reactant remaining after various reaction times. The analyses that have been given here have been based on the simplest type of rate equation, i.e., equations corresponding to first-order reactions. In later studies you will find that more complicated rate equations are often required to describe the dependence of the rate of the reactions on the concentrations of the reagents. But procedures similar to those that you have studied here can still be used to deduce the rate equation and the rate constant from the concentration v. time data.

It should be mentioned that more complete studies of the rates of chemical reactions will show that reactions generally proceed much faster at higher temperatures and, therefore, that the rate constant in the rate equation is a function of temperature. Investigations of this temperature dependence (in addition to the concentration dependence of the rate with which we have been concerned here) provide further insight into the nature of the reaction process by which one compound is chemically transformed into another.